MY ANIMALS
AND ME

Other Seabury Books by Nan Hayden Agle:

MAPLE STREET

TARR OF BELWAY SMITH

KISH'S COLT

JOE BEAN

KATE AND THE APPLE TREE

THE INGENIOUS JOHN BANVARD
(with Frances Atchinson Bacon)

MY ANIMALS AND ME

An Autobiographical Story by Nan Hayden Agle

Photographs by Emily Hayden

THE SEABURY PRESS • NEW YORK

Thanks to:

Elizabeth Foreman Lewis, who
wanted me to write about my
animals; Morrell Gipson;
Laura Kassos; Jim Giblin; and
all of the people and animals at Nancy's Fancy.

For my sisters Ruth and Catherine

whose memories will not be the same as mine, I'll bet;

and for my granddaughter Kim.

CONTENTS

MY ANIMALS
AND ME

one

IMPORTANT NEWS

DURING RECESS AT SCHOOL on Friday, March the seventh, 1913, I heard some news that I couldn't wait to tell. As soon as the three-thirty bell rang I hopped on my bicycle and sailed down the road. Home was only a mile and a half from school and all downhill, so I was there in no time.

"Mother," I shouted, bursting into the house and tossing my books on the hall table, "I'm home! Where are you?"

Liza, who had been with us since before Mother was born, came to the dining room door and said, "She's in the dark room, Miss Nan. She'll be down directly."

That wasn't soon enough. I bounded up the front stairs and down the hall to the dark room, which was also the bathroom.

"Mother, let me in," I said, pressing my cheek against the closed door. "I have something important to tell you."

"Seven, eight, nine—" Mother counted aloud, "don't open the door yet, dear. Give me five minutes."

I sat down at the top of the back stairs and tapped my feet impatiently. Five minutes is a long time to wait anywhere when you are full of news. Especially in a pitch-black hall. I couldn't see a thing as the hall light was off and all the bedroom doors closed. Mother didn't want any light to spoil the plate she was developing.

Mother was an artist. Her water color paintings of wild flowers and outdoor scenes were beautiful. Mostly, though, she liked to take pictures with her big square camera. Then she would develop the plates, print the prints, retouch them, and sign them E.H.H.

Daddy, a lawyer, liked to graft things. He would splice a tree limb, set in a twig with a bud on it, and the bud would grow.

My sister Catherine was the best actress in the sixth grade, and Ruth, my other sister, a student at Goucher College, was excellent at everything.

I liked animals and I didn't have a single one of my own, which is why my news was so terribly important.

I knocked on the door—surely five minutes were up by now.

"You may come in if you come quickly," Mother said.

I slipped into the dark room, my white middy blouse turning pink in the eerie glow of the red light hanging over the hand basin. I sat down on the edge of the tub, pink too, and said in a loud voice, "Peanuts is for sale!"

"Peanuts?"

Mother turned toward me looking like a short spook, pink highlights rippling up and down her wet rubber apron. "Oh, Beany Schlens' donkey, of course."

"Yes. Imagine selling your own donkey. But, Mother, this is the important part: I want him. Jack and Bob are Daddy's dogs. The chickens are his, too, except for the bantams, Billy and Jenny, which are Catherine's, and all the wild things—rabbits, squirrels, chipmunks—are yours. I don't have one single solitary animal, not *one*."

"Well, Nan, you'll have to ask your father about the donkey."

"You mean you are willing if he is?" I slid off the tub full of hope.

"I'm not sure," Mother answered, rocking the pan of developer fluid gently with both hands. "You know how you are about animals."

"Yes. That's the whole point. A donkey would be a perfect pet. He's not like a bird in a cage dying to fly, or a fish swimming around in a bowl dreaming of the open sea. He doesn't eat anybody and nobody eats him."

Mother nodded and I added, "Ask Daddy for me."

I wasn't much on talking to my father. I wanted to but couldn't. Still, the silences between us were very friendly and he sometimes talked to me about what he was interested in, such as mathematics, stars in the sky, Maryland Indians, and most of all Nancy's Fancy, our place. (Some people thought because my name was Nan it was named for me, but it wasn't. The name was there long before we were, so Daddy said.) He had light-brown curly hair and marvelous muscles from doing gymnastics at the Baltimore Athletic Club and pushing the wheel hoe in the garden.

"You'd better ask about the donkey, yourself," Mother told me. "Now run along. I have two more plates to develop. Liza will give you something to eat."

I left the dark room and went down the narrow back steps to the kitchen, which was by far the largest room in the house. It had windows on both sides and a huge brick fireplace with a coal stove in it.

Liza was stirring something on the stove. Her face was calm and brown, and she wore a full skirt over so many petticoats you could crack black walnuts on a flat iron turned upside down on her lap and she'd hardly feel it.

She laid the long-handled spoon on the wooden table and gave me a slice of homemade bread still warm from the oven, with butter and brown sugar on top.

Between bites I told her about Peanuts. Just as I got to the end of the telling, Catherine came home and I had to start over again.

"If Daddy does buy the donkey I know who will take care of him," my sister said, reaching for her slice of bread.

"*I* will," was my quick and positive answer.

Everybody was forever saying Catherine did all the work at Nancy's Fancy, mainly because she was so willing and so good at doing things. She helped Daddy weed, plant, and spray the fruit trees. She bagged grapes to keep the bees off, and she posed for Mother and her picture-taking friends.

Even so, she did not do all the work. Lots of times I set the table for dinner and helped wipe dishes. And if the weather was warm enough to go barefoot I helped wash the front porch, sliding in the cool hose water, which was fun. I didn't help at all, though, when

Daddy

Mother

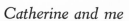

Ruth

Catherine and me

Liza

my neck was out of kilter.

Sometimes, not often, say once or twice a year maybe, I'd get a stiff neck and the worst earache. It'd hurt so much I couldn't go to sleep unless Mother's hand was on the pillow under my ear. One good thing though—I couldn't remember the hurt once it stopped, not even for five minutes.

"A donkey won't be much trouble no matter who takes care of him," I told Catherine. "During the day he'll be out in the field or tied to a tree on a long rope where he can eat grass and always have water and shade, we'll see to that. Nighttime in the box stall he won't make much manure, and anyway I like donkey manure better than chicken manure."

"I do, too," my sister said, "much better."

Liza shooed us out of the kitchen, saying such talk would make our grandparents turn over in their graves.

Although both grandparents on Mother's side of the family, the Southern side, had been dead since we were born, we knew them well through Liza. According to her they were perfect. She measured us against them and we always fell short.

Daddy's father was dead, too. His mother wasn't though. But this was no time to be thinking about grandparents.

Catherine and I walked down to the barn to look things over with the donkey in mind, both talking at once. The barn, built on a hill, had a large carriage room on the uphill side where all of the children in the neighborhood played on rainy days. The back room was a shop.

I stuck my head through the little door; the big doors were closed. "The cart can go there, the harness over there, and the saddle on that rack," I said, pointing. "Come on, let's go down in the stable and see where he'll sleep."

"No," Catherine said, turning around. "You're counting on that donkey too much. Even if Daddy says yes, he may already have been sold. Donkeys are scarce, you know."

"He's *got* to be mine. I'll ask Daddy as soon as he gets home from town," I called after her as she walked back to the house.

Then I went in the barn, down the steps to the dimly lighted stable below, walked past the empty open stalls, and stopped in front of the box stall.

I could almost see long ears over the door.

I lifted the rusty latch and opened the door. A haunted damp moldy smell came up from the earth floor and I thought I heard a ghost horse stamp in the shadow by the manger.

"Catherine, wait for me!" I shouted and raced up the steps.

She'd already gone in the house. Out in the sunlight I knew it wasn't a ghost horse—probably the rooster or even nothing.

The nunnery bell struck five o'clock; Daddy would be home in half an hour. I liked to hear the bell, clear and close. The grounds of the nunnery, Mount de Sales Academy, went all around the back of Nancy's Fancy, and the north side too.

I walked along the brick path beside the house, around the front circle, down the driveway to the gate, and climbed up on the gatepost to wait. I wished Catherine hadn't said donkeys were scarce.

A wagon went by, the hoofs of the big horse clop, clopping. An automobile went the other way. There weren't many autos in Catonsville, Maryland. Mr. Yardley, our minister at St. Timothy's Episcopal Church, had one, though.

Finally the five-thirty streetcar came, the overhead trolley sending

off sparks on the curve. It stopped at our gate and Daddy got off as he did every single weekday. Eight-fifteen going to town, five-thirty coming home; you could set your watch by him.

As he crossed the road slapping his leg with the newspaper, Jack, the little black and tan, and Bob, the collie, raced to meet him. I jumped down to meet him too. On the way up the drive, Daddy taking one long stride to three of mine, I did not mention the donkey as I had planned. After dinner would be a better time.

When dinner was over, Mother and Daddy reading in front of the open fire in the living room, the dogs asleep at Daddy's feet, I told him.

He listened attentively, looking at me through his spectacles with clear hazel eyes, holding the bowl of his slim, black pipe in his hand. There never was a better listener. After I explained how much fun it would be to own a donkey, how I'd wanted a pet for years, how the back field was full of grass or would be soon, and the barn empty except for chickens, he turned to Mother and said, "I take it this business about the jackass is pretty serious, Emily."

Mother smiled, her black eyes extra bright. I corrected him, saying, "Donkey, Daddy, not jackass, and there is no time to lose as donkeys are scarce."

He looked at me as though I were some sort of rare plant he'd never seen before, then reached for the *Scientific American* again and began to read, not saying he'd think about it or anything. Mother said something about a gray donkey making a nice touch on the landscape, and she began to read too.

There wasn't a bit of use in my saying any more. With Daddy you stated your case and that was that. He either would or wouldn't.

The next day, Saturday, still not saying a word about the donkey, he pruned the blackberry bushes and I hung around hoping. First I cleared my throat off and on to let him know I was there. Then, when I couldn't stand it another minute, I hinted, "If we had a donkey around here and a wagon I could haul the cut briars away and dump them on the burnt pile." Mr. Kreger, who lived in the little stone house between our house and the barn, had called it the burnt pile and before long that was its name.

Nothing came of the hint.

Not knowing the answer to something and not being able to do one thing about it really tires you out. By suppertime I was exhausted. Around eight o'clock that night when I thought I had to know about the donkey or burst, Daddy telephoned Mr. Griffith, one of my best friends. He and his wonderful white horse, Mag, did our plowing.

"Griffith," Daddy said. I was sitting on the bottom step in the hall listening. "This is Charles Hayden speaking. Would you have some time to do a favor for me one day next week? Fine. Thank you. I bought a jackass from—"

Without waiting to hear the rest, I bolted through the front door, leaped off the porch, and raced down the lawn. Joyously flapping my arms and yelling "Hoo-ray, hoo-ray!" at the top of my lungs, I circled the big pine tree three times. Then I ran back to the house and into the kitchen.

"What did Daddy say about the donkey?" asked Catherine, looking up from *Pickwick Papers*, which she was reading to Liza.

"He said yes," Mother answered for me from the dining room door. Daddy, pleased as anything, was looking over her shoulder.

I wanted to hug him but didn't. Catherine was the hugger in the family. Instead I said, "Thank you, Daddy," and gave him a grateful look.

Liza laughed softly to herself, covering her mouth with her old, old hand. Catherine said it would be peachy to have a donkey at Nancy's Fancy. "Peachy" was the rage at school; everybody was saying it.

Right then the back door opened and Mr. Kreger came in, his oily gray hair slicked to one side, small light blue eyes watery and squinty under sparse gray eyebrows, a wisp of a goatee on his chin. You could tell by his expression he was wondering what in the world the whole family was doing in the kitchen at that hour.

Liza frowned. She didn't think much of Mr. Kreger. He cut grass and things like that for us, and ate in our kitchen at his own table under the side window. Liza cooked his meals but wouldn't sit down with him because he picked his teeth and belched. "Buzzard," she'd say when he did.

Daddy told Mr. Kreger the news and added, "Now you and the

jackass can help Griffith with the plowing."

Mr. Kreger reached for the lid lifter, took the lid off of the front hole of the stove, spat tobacco juice on the coals, and said, "I got *no* use for a mule."

"Peanuts is not a mule or a jackass," I said with dignity. "And he is not a workhorse either. He is my pet donkey."

And it was true, really true!

two

PEANUTS

AS DADDY DID NOT LIKE things haphazard, he arranged a schedule for the next week. Monday and Tuesday Catherine and I were to clean the box stall and whitewash the walls. Mr. Kreger refused to do one thing. Wednesday, the Davis Feed Store in Catonsville was to deliver a bale of hay, a bushel of oats, and a bale of straw for bedding. Thursday was a spare day in case it was needed, and Friday Mr. Griffith was to drive Mag, hitched to his wagon, over to Beany's house, tie Peanuts on behind, hitched to the donkey cart, and bring him to our house.

The week started as planned. Monday after school Catherine and

I dragged porch chairs out of the box stall, squirted them off with the hose, and put them on the front porch. The boards stacked beside the manger we stored in Mr. Kreger's basement room.

Tuesday we scraped the box stall floor, a job I can tell you, and hauled I don't know how many wheelbarrow loads of dirt to Daddy's compost pile at the edge of the nunnery woods.

Wednesday we brushed the stone walls hard and whitewashed them. Mr. Kreger wouldn't even help us carry the heavy bag of lime down the steps. We were running a day late by now and the order from the feed store was too. It didn't come.

Thursday, a cold rainy miserable day, things really went off schedule. The order still didn't come and Peanuts did.

When I got home from school there he was tied to the clothesline post near the kitchen door, the dogs barking their heads off at him, Liza calling from the back door, "Here Jack, here Bob, you come in the house this minute," neither one minding.

I clapped my hands, stamped my foot, and shouted "Quit!" so loud the dogs, still barking, ran to the kitchen door and skidded through.

Peanuts didn't look happy even with no dogs barking at him. His head was hanging down as far as the rope would let it. His ears, long as from your elbow to your fingertips, were drooping and rain trickled down his gray face and gray sides. More drops dripped off of his tail.

He was absolutely wonderful, larger than a pony, smaller than a horse, and mine.

I rushed at him with open arms, my heart pounding.

He flattened his ears against his head and looked at me with as wicked a gleam in his large brown eyes as I had ever seen, and I had seen some furious gleams during fights on the playground at school when no teacher was looking.

I backed away shouting, "Catherine, Mother, Liza, help!"

Liza came to the door and said, "Miss Catherine hasn't come from school yet and your mother is at a church meeting. Nobody's here except Grandma."

"Grandma!" I said in dismay. "Rain, donkey, no bedding, no hay, no oats—and now Grandma!"

Grandma, Daddy's mother, lived ten miles away in Baltimore with her daughter, Caroline our aunt. They came to see us on Thursdays, some Sundays, and all holidays, and for some reason, always brought out the worst in Catherine and me. Liza said it was because they had come from the North where people were more "formal."

Now Liza gave me a reproachful look. "You know well as I do Grandma and Auntie come every last Thursday. Auntie isn't here yet but Grandma is sewing in the living room by herself and you'd better go in there and pay your respects."

"I can't right now, Liza. I've got to take care of my donkey."

"Mr. Griffith says he put the cart in the barn out of the weather. But the donkey wouldn't go a step further than where he is, no indeed," Liza told me.

"Poor boy, sold, doesn't know us or his new home, and this awful rain. He'll catch his death of cold, Liza. We must do something."

Mr. Kreger made me so mad. He was standing in the doorway of his house grinning and spitting streams of tobacco juice, enough to ruin the grass under the cherry tree.

"You couldn't kill that dang mule with a double blast of dynamite," he said, adding a "he, he, he" that infuriated me.

I didn't answer him. Instead I got two umbrellas from the house and opened them, being especially careful with the silver-handled black silk one that I presumed was Grandma's. Standing as close to Peanuts as I dared, I held the umbrellas over as much of him as I could.

Never was I gladder to see my sister Catherine.

"Isn't he marvelous?" I said, lowering my aching arms for a second's rest.

"Peachy."

"Lead him to the barn for me this once, please," I said. "He doesn't like me yet."

He didn't like Catherine either. She had to back away too. However, she held one of the umbrellas until Daddy came home, which was a great help.

All animals and people respected my father, and Peanuts was no exception. He looked Daddy in the eye and walked to the barn beside him, stepping daintily with his small, neat, shiny black hoofs, down the hill, through the barnyard gate, and into the box stall.

I hated to leave him in a bare stall with not a single bit of bedding on the floor, his first night at his new home.

One thing for sure, he wasn't going to bed hungry. Liza helped us round up a light supper for him: corn flakes, toast, string beans, celery, lettuce, laying mash, and cookies, enough to tide him over until morning.

Collecting his supper and giving it to him, standing on a box outside the stall and leaning way over to reach the manger, took time and made us late for ours.

We were supposed to be on time for every meal and to sit straight

Daddy in his barn shop, testing a plane

with backs away from chairs. I kissed Grandma and Auntie lightly on the cheek and took my place next to Mother. Catherine's chair was next to Daddy at the foot of the table.

Grandma was big and handsome with a pompadour of beautiful white hair on top of her head. She had on a long, black silk dress that rustled and she smelled of lavender and spice.

Auntie, slim as Grandma was stout, wore a plain black skirt tightly belted and a white, high-necked, long-sleeved blouse, a gold pin at the throat. Her face was so sensitive she always looked as though her feelings were about to be hurt. Auntie was a schoolteacher, ninth grade at a public school in town. She had written an arithmetic book that was used in the schools and she wanted to go to Venice. She felt about Venice the way I did about Peanuts.

Conversation went back and forth across the table but I didn't listen to it. My mind was too full of other things. Once during a lull I said, "I'm glad we managed to keep the donkey somewhat dry with the two umbrellas." Evidently there had been words said about Grandma's umbrella being wet, for Liza, serving more rolls, poked me in the back, the signal to drop the subject. Then she hurried around behind Mother and poked her, which meant change the subject.

"Charles," Mother said, "give Grandma a slice of roast from the other side where it is nice and brown."

I was always glad when Grandma and Auntie went home, and terribly ashamed of being glad because they were very fond of us, Daddy the most, Catherine next because she looked like him. And we were very fond of them only you couldn't feel completely free when they were there. I was particularly glad when they left that day because I was worn out.

"Poor Peanuts alone in the barn with no bedding, not a soul near him except the chickens," I said to Catherine after we'd settled for the night in our white iron double bed with brass knobs, Catherine on the window side, me next to the door.

"It's only for one night," she answered and I said, "Let's get up early and let him run in the field. Want to?"

"Yes."

Catherine was great at saying yes.

The next morning I ran ahead of her and opened the gate between the barnyard and the field, propped it open for Peanuts. Then I ran into the stable to open the box stall door to let him out. Through a wide crack in the door I saw a shiny eye and over the door two ears.

"Ca-thrin," I yelled, "come here!"

She came right away down the barn steps.

"*You*'d better let him out this first time," I told her as I climbed to a safe place in the manger of the next stall.

The second the box stall door swung open, Peanuts shot out like a bullet. He circled the barnyard scaring the daylights out of the chickens, feathers floating down like snow. Gay irridescent Billy and plain little brown Jenny, the bantam pair, took to the limb of the walnut tree that stuck out over the fence. The big rooster squawked and squawked.

All of a sudden Peanuts noticed the open gate, bolted through and charged down the field ninety miles an hour. At the end of the field way down by the road, he stopped short to heehaw at a passing streetcar. Then he turned, and with head down and tail out straight he headed for us.

No two people ever went over a fence faster than Catherine and I did.

Near the spring where honeysuckle had pulled the fence low, Peanuts sailed over himself—a beautiful jump.

"Daddy, Mother, Mr. Kreger," we yelled as we ran to the house, "the donkey is loose!"

Thank goodness Peanuts stopped in the middle of the front lawn to roll and kick all four legs in the air. As he got up with a satisfied grunt, Daddy grabbed him by the halter and led him back to the box stall.

We didn't want to leave him there with nothing to eat and still no bedding but we had to go to school. Mother said she'd feed him as soon as the order came, and after what Daddy said to Mr. Davis

Mr. Kreger's house

over the telephone it would be there soon.

As I was strapping my books on the luggage carrier of my bicycle I asked Mr. Kreger to please pull some dried grass for Peanuts. He didn't answer. He was an utterly selfish man and he always smelled of patent medicines and snuff. The cupboard in his house was full of medicine bottles, all sizes and colors. We were not supposed to go in his house because that would violate his privacy, which my father considered a sin. But one rainy day, when Mr. Kreger had gone to Hagerstown to visit his sister, Catherine and I went in anyway and snooped around. We opened his cupboard door, saw the bottles and smelled them, pretending they were poison.

Catherine and I talked about Mr. Kreger as we pumped hard on the long, uphill pull to school, our bikes swaying from side to side. We said over and over how mean he was.

Most of the time I liked school. That day, though, things did not go too well. Miss Smith, our teacher, sent me to the office for talking to my best friend Robbins Rich during Arithmetic. Robbins was a beautiful girl, by far the prettiest in the whole school. She had long black curls and wore a bandeau with pompoms on the side. Her eyes were violets and her cheeks peaches and cream.

When I told Mr. De Russey, the principal, all about Peanuts he said it was no wonder I couldn't stop talking, which showed what a fine person he was. Miss Smith was fine too, a great woman really. It was my fault she lost her temper. Mr. De Russey told me to go back to our room and tell her I was sorry, which I was, and to keep quiet the rest of the day, which I did, although it was not easy.

When Catherine and I zoomed home, practically everybody in the neighborhood was waiting for us at the side gate, wanting a ride in the donkey cart. Will and David were draped across the low limb of the wild plum tree. Will's sister Dot, a small eight-year-old girl with lots of flying-around dark hair, was sitting on the side bench talking to Gladys, the funniest girl anywhere without meaning to be. Billy, Howard, and Landon were on their hands and knees hunting for a nickel somebody had dropped in the grass, finders keepers.

After collecting apples and ginger snaps from Liza at the door we headed for the barn.

Catherine picked up the bridle and ran down the hill to the field, with the rest of us right behind her.

"Isn't he great?" I said, pointing to Peanuts standing under the walnut tree, tail our way.

"He looks all right," David said, hiking up his knickers and tightening his belt. "I'll let you know how great he is after our ride. Let's get going. I don't have all day to stall around."

"Here, Peanuts, come on, boy," Catherine called sweetly, sugar lumps in one hand, bridle in the other.

Peanuts raised his head, ears pointed with interest. Taking his time, he sauntered over to us.

"Nice sugar, see," Catherine said, holding out her hand.

He stretched his long neck way out, scooped up the sugar with his upper lip, one eye on the bridle.

"Grab his halter," Billy yelled and Peanuts reared. After that, Catherine couldn't get near him. He was too smart for her.

"You stand over there against the fence, Catherine," David ordered. "We'll herd him your way. Come on everybody, line up."

We lined up, Gladys on one end, Dot on the other, closed ranks and advanced. Peanuts enjoyed the maneuver for a short time, then cut around Gladys and galloped to the middle of the field.

"Surround him," said Billy, giving Dot a push.

Peanuts allowed us to get fairly close, then kicked out with both heels; we dashed for the gate, falling over one another trying to get out first. We all made it through the gate except Will, who got confused, ran the other way, and climbed a young sassafras tree. It swayed with him, skinny as he was, and he shouted, "Catherine, save me!" She was the one everybody called in an emergency.

"Stay put, Will," she shouted back. "He'll get bored soon."

While the others hung around waiting for Peanuts to get bored, Catherine and I went to the barn, forked straw in his bed—the order had finally come—poured two scoops of oats in the manger and dropped hay through the trap door. It fell softly on the stones below, next to the chicken house door where Peanuts couldn't help finding it.

When we joined the others again, Peanuts was wandering over toward the woods.

"He's bored now, Will," Catherine shouted. "If you hurry you can make it."

Will climbed down from the tree slowly, cautiously, looking around at Peanuts. Peanuts pretended not to see him and sauntered the other way. He let Will get halfway to the gate, then turned and rushed him through. It was beautifully funny to see, such speed and such a sense of humor—Peanuts', not Will's. Will went right home without saying a word.

"Some donkey ride, I don't think," David said when he stopped laughing enough to say anything.

"Things will be different soon," I explained as we walked up the hill. "You can't expect him to trust us right away. Before long he will. Before long he'll come to Catherine and let her put the bridle over his ears. You'll see."

"Well, I'm not holding my breath until then," David declared. "A whole afternoon wasted if you ask me. We might as well go home; it's too late for kick-the-can or baseball or anything."

Catherine and I watched the others go. I was disappointed we hadn't gotten a ride, and at the same time I wasn't. The way things had turned out, I felt I knew Peanuts much better. He really was very smart, and funny too.

"Think he'll let us hitch up tomorrow?" I asked Catherine hopefully.

"Maybe."

Neither of us guessed what that first ride would be like.

three

THE FIRST RIDE
AND A LITTLE BIT
OF PLOWING

THE NEXT DAY, Saturday, Daddy caught Peanuts for us, put the bridle on with no trouble at all, led him up the hill, and held him while Catherine and I hitched him to the cart. It was a two-wheeler with basket-weave top.

After standing back to see the whole effect, which was superb, we hopped in and the first ride began, Catherine holding the reins,

Daddy leading the donkey.

"Look at us, Liza," we called out as we passed the kitchen porch. She waved from the door, and we went on around the house and stopped on the circle. Mother took our picture, her big camera up on its tripod legs.

"One more in case somebody moved," she said, disappearing under the black headcloth. "Hold it, hold it!"

Catherine and I were grinning, Peanuts looking straight at the camera, when she squeezed the bulb, *click*, a second time.

That was a good one.

"Let go now, Daddy, and get out of his way fast," Catherine said, sitting straight, ready for anything. "He may dash. Hold on tight, Nan."

Daddy let go, I grabbed the seat under me with both hands, and Peanuts stood there.

"Get up," Catherine said, slapping the reins on his rump.

He lowered his head and walked slowly down the driveway, slowly out the gate, and more slowly still up the lane. The slow creaking of the wheels turning and the tap-tap-tap of his hoofs almost put us to sleep before we reached Gladys's gate.

"Hi, Gladys." I waved to her sitting on her porch. "Want to take a ride?"

Of course she did.

"Whoa."

Peanuts was an excellent whoaer. So excellent, in fact, that after Gladys got in the cart he refused to go on.

"I guess you'll have to get out," Catherine told her. "He can barely pull two of us, let alone three."

Gladys didn't mind. She was that kind of a girl—used to losing races, "it" in a lot of games, and last to be chosen in a choose-up-sides.

Peanuts went on, step-step-step, head down, tail swinging like a pendulum.

"He really is slow," I said. "Let me drive for a while."

It was glorious to be driving my own donkey, even if he was slow as molasses. I don't think we would have made it up the second hill, which was rather steep, if Landon and Billy hadn't come along. They pushed, grunting and laughing, tongues hanging out on purpose.

Finally we reached the Mount de Sales gate.

"As it took so long to get this far I think we'd better turn around and start back, don't you?" Catherine asked, and Billy said, "If you want to be home for Christmas you sure better." He and Landon laughed so hard at that, they had to sit down.

I pulled on the left-hand rein. Peanuts turned slowly. For one second he stood tall, then he lit out for home, fast, down the hill, the cart swaying from side to side, wheels spinning, hoofs sending off sparks.

"Whoa, whoa!" Catherine yelled, grabbing the reins from me and pulling back on them, hard. "Whoa!"

Holding on to the sides of the cart, I yelled with her, and Billy and Landon ran after us laughing and shouting, "Come on, Peanuts!" He was going so fast they soon gave up.

Peanuts passed Gladys's house at a full gallop, bit in his teeth, the cart first on one wheel then on the other. When he reached our front gate he was going so fast he didn't even see it, galloped right on by and down Edmondson Avenue.

Peanuts was an excellent whoaer

There was a steam roller parked at the end of Mr. Griffith's lane. Peanuts saw that, swerved to the right and dashed through our side gate, wide enough for a donkey but not for a cart.

The wheels struck the post—*wham!*—the traces let go, the shafts flew up, the cart tipped back and dumped us out. I turned a backward somersault, landing in the road. Catherine went through the air and came down nose first on the gravel. Peanuts, traces flying behind him, raced up the side path, cut across behind Mr. Kreger's house, and headed for the barn.

As I picked myself up, rubbing my scratched elbows, I saw him jump over the fence into his own field.

"Imagine him being so smart, knowing where he lives this soon," I said proudly.

Evidently Catherine was pretty well shaken up. She didn't say anything.

Daddy must have seen the accident or heard the crash because he came down the path almost as fast as Peanuts went up.

"Anybody hurt?" he asked, and you could see he really was relieved when Catherine said, "Slightly."

She and I limped up to the house and out to the kitchen where Liza bathed our wounds.

Later when we were in the living room reading and resting up from the crash, Mr. Kreger went by the window pulling the donkey cart and grumbling to himself. Still later, during dinner Daddy told Mother he was going to give Peanuts a lesson first thing in the morning, one he would not soon forget.

Right after breakfast he started for the barn, a determined look on his face. I went along feeling slightly uneasy.

Daddy opened the big barn doors, propped them back with rocks, and hauled out the plow.

"What are you going to do with *that?*" I asked, hands on my hips. "Mr. Griffith and Mag aren't going to plow on Sunday, are they?"

"Peanuts is going to plow the west field for red clover," was the answer.

"A little pet donkey pull that great big heavy plow? It'll strain his back," I said with alarm. "Mag is three times his size and she has to pull hard as anything when she's plowing."

By that time Catherine was there, dressed for Sunday school. Mother had said as Peanuts was so new I could stay home with him this once.

"Let the donkey plow, Nan," Catherine said. "It will do him good.

He's strong as a horse and he needs to work."

"Oh, all right. I'll let him plow a little bit but not enough to tire him out." I sat down on the ground, bolt upright, arms folded.

Catherine went on back to the house and along came Mr. Kreger in his Sunday pants, shoes shined, purple shirt, suspenders, and striped tie. He eyed Daddy and the plow and laughed, "He, he, he."

Ignoring him, Daddy went down the hill with the bridle in his hand.

Mr. Kreger went up the hill to the rock pile under the black walnut tree and sat there looking as though he were waiting for a sideshow to begin.

Before long, shouts came from the barnyard. More shouts followed, then Peanuts and Daddy charged up the hill, Peanuts' ears flat against his head, Daddy leaning to windward, trying to keep up with the donkey and not fall down.

I got up hurriedly to give them plenty of room and Daddy shouted, "Kreger, give me a hand with the jackass while I hitch him to the plow."

Mr. Kreger wouldn't go near Peanuts. Daddy got so angry his face and neck turned real red. For a moment I was afraid he might tell Mr. Kreger to get off the place and stay off. He almost had once before for something or other. But mother had said, "You can't fire him, Charles. Where would he go? What would he do? Nobody else on earth would put up with him."

Daddy soon cooled down and tied Peanuts to the latch of the door.

"Good idea, Daddy," I called out to encourage him and he said, "I wish you would go back to the house, Nan, and let me handle this alone."

As he didn't actually tell me to leave, I stayed.

Daddy put the collar and traces on Peanuts, then hooked on the plow.

Peanuts stepped out bravely, dragging the heavy plow over on its side. I was proud of him and said so. At the edge of the red clover field near the grape arbor Daddy righted the plow. The instant the blade dug into the earth Peanuts stopped and stayed stopped. When Daddy shouted, "Get up, get up!" and slapped him with the reins, Peanuts turned around and gave him a cool, bored look.

"He's saying no, Daddy," I said.

On the rock pile Mr. Kreger laughed until he choked.

Daddy took his penknife out of his pocket, the sharpest penknife anywhere, and cut a long, wicked sassafras sucker.

"Please don't switch him," I pleaded, jumping up and down. I was sure he wouldn't as he never spanked us—pretty sure, that is.

He flung the switch toward Mr. Kreger, not at him, just his way.

"He, he, he."

Then Peanuts stepped back, getting his left hind leg caught over the traces. For some time Daddy struggled to free it, sweat pouring off of his forehead. I sympathized with him and told him so. Manipulating a donkey's hind leg is not only difficult to do, it is dangerous. Finally Daddy gave up, unhooked the plow, and led Peanuts back to the barnyard.

I didn't say anything at all right then, thinking it best not to. But as we walked to the house I said, "Give him another chance, Daddy. He's so fond of you, fonder than of anybody else, and anybody can make two mistakes." I meant first dumping us out of the cart and then not plowing.

Much later in the afternoon Daddy told me he would give him one more chance with the cart, not the plow.

"Thank you," I said, "but the plowing wasn't a total loss."

"No?"

"No. I learned something about Peanuts I didn't know before. When he wants to be, he's a match for you, Daddy. With patience, though, I believe you'll win."

"Come to think of it," Daddy said, amusement looking out of his eyes, "I learned something about myself. It will take all I can muster to tie for first place."

four

HELP! MURDER! POLICE!

DADDY'S SECOND CHANCE with Peanuts was set for the next Saturday. That morning when Catherine and I gave the donkey his breakfast we noticed a silence in the barnyard. Usually the chickens were scratching around and clucking.

"It certainly is quiet around here and I don't see a chicken anywhere," Catherine said.

"Maybe Mr. Kreger forgot to let them out."

No, the little hen high door was open.

Catherine went into the henhouse, the hen room really, a room opposite the foot of the barn steps. "Nan," she called out, "come here and look!"

I pushed past her and a cold chill washed over me. On the stone floor under the roost lay a pile of chicken heads, white ruffled collars stained blood red.

All of Daddy's pretty White Leghorns were dead, their eyes glassy and half closed.

We ran to the house yelling, "Help, murder, police!" which brought Mr. Kreger out of his house on the run. "Who, what happened?" he wanted to know and you could tell he hoped for the worst.

"The chickens are dead," we told him, and bursting into the kitchen we said it again, loud.

"Billy and Jenny, too?" asked Mother, hurrying down the hall, a platinum print in one hand, retouching brush in the other.

Billy and Jenny? Catherine gasped and covered her mouth with both hands.

We raced back to the barn, Bob and Jack bounding on ahead of us, Mr. Kreger right behind us, and Daddy behind him.

"Be careful, Charles," Mother called from the kitchen door, "the thieves might still be there, hiding in the barn."

Daddy was calm. He always was except when plowing with Peanuts. "Don't touch anything," he said when he saw the pitiful pile of heads. "This is a matter for the police."

Bob and Jack sniffed the still damp blood, and Catherine and I stooped to look closely for two small heads.

"I don't see either one of them," I said sadly.

"I do!" Catherine shouted. "There they are," and she pointed to the top roost. "See them?"

Way over in the dark corner I saw two small humps, Billy and

Jenny, alive with their heads on. Tears of joy stung my eyes and in an instant I felt the terrible difference between life and death. Catherine must have felt it too, because she took my hand and I was not a take-by-the-hand person.

"They saw what happened and they can't tell us," I said. Dogs could tell you a lot with their tails and eyes, donkeys with ears and heels, but chickens just didn't communicate much except about the sun coming up or about laying eggs.

Billy and Jenny understood a hammer though. Bang on an anvil with one and see how fast they'd come, wings out, head low, feet skimming over the ground, sure somebody was cracking black walnuts.

Mr. Kreger shook his head and said over and over, "Who could a done it, Mr. Hayden? Who could a wrung the necks of them pretty white chickens?" He really was sorry.

Daddy was both sorry and angry. "I'll catch those thieves if it is the last thing I do," he said.

Just then Peanuts came to the door and looked in, curious to see what was going on, and Mr. Kreger waved his arms at him rudely, saying, "Get out of here, mule," spoiling his one tender moment over the chickens.

Daddy led Peanuts to the field and closed the gate so he couldn't trample the evidence in the barnyard. Then we all went up to the house and Daddy telephoned the police.

The daytime policeman, Mr. Pohlman, arrived on the ten-fifteen streetcar. Catonsville had two policemen, day and night, so the village and outlying areas were protected at all times. We didn't have many serious crimes in the village as a rule, though once a strange woman was shot by a man from out of town. Her body was found on the golf course and one of the boys at school said he heard she was wearing a pink dress trimmed in lace.

Mr. Pohlman and Daddy talked over what Daddy called the "corpus delicti," which he said was a big word for "what happened." Then they went down to the barn still talking, flinging out arms and that sort of thing, Daddy smoking his pipe furiously. Naturally Catherine, Mr. Kreger, the dogs, and I went along.

The whole time we were standing over the heads, going over the gory details for the fifty-fifth time, Peanuts stood lonesome at the gate braying, "Oink-eee, oink-ee, oink," adding a dismal note to an already dismal occasion.

Mr. Pohlman examined the bloody heads, shook his own, and asked time of theft, number of chickens, value of same. He wrote the answers Daddy gave him in a black book resting on his knee, his foot on the first roost.

Thirty-seven hens and one rooster, approximately a dollar apiece. I thought about that, then thought about Peanuts and his value. To me he was priceless.

Mr. Kreger, eyes on the policeman, kept switching an ample quid of tobacco from one cheek to the other. You could see it plain as day, like a mole underground.

Out in the barnyard Mr. Pohlman found one clear footprint that turned out to match Mr. Kreger's shoe, plenty of donkey prints, and webs of feathery chicken prints all over the place, the last the White Leghorns would ever make.

We walked back to the house and as Mr. Pohlman left he said, "Mr. Hayden, we'll catch the thieves. They have to sell the chickens before they spoil and when they do we'll nab them."

Mother was back in the kitchen comforting Liza. Poor Liza. She was sitting by the kitchen table, her hands folded in her lap, her head bent down. When I came into the room she was saying to Mother, shaking her head, "I don't know what the world is coming to, Miss Emily, people stealing your chickens while you sleep, robbers walking by right under your window in the dead of night."

I could see those robbers in my mind's eye—two of them dressed in black, masks over their eyes, hats pulled down, tiptoeing past the house in dirty tennis shoes, full heavy sacks on their backs, blood dripping down on their heels.

Naturally with all the excitement Daddy did not hitch Peanuts to the donkey cart as planned. In fact nobody even mentioned it. That day and Sunday everybody just hung around the house feeling subdued, even the dogs.

Monday, before we left for school, the telephone rang and Daddy answered. After listening, he nodded his head and said, "Good work, Pohlman, you deserve a promotion." Then he hung up the receiver and turned to Mother. "The police caught the thieves red-handed in Lexington Market, Emily, two of them."

"Good," Mother said.

It was good but it didn't bring back the chickens and they had liked living very much. And now Peanuts would be terribly lonely, only Billy and Jenny in the barn with him and they were gone all day, roaming all over the place.

"Peanuts needs a friend to live with him, some kind, gentle animal with a good disposition and a small appetite," I told Catherine as we were getting ready for bed that night. She agreed and I added, "What animal? And where can we get one?"

She didn't know but she said she bet anything Mr. Griffith would.

The next afternoon Peanuts was so docile I decided to ride him donkeyback over to Mr. Griffith's.

Catherine saddled him for me, pulling the belly strap tight, and boosted me on. There I was, riding donkeyback for the first time, my feet in the bell-shaped leather stirrups, my knees hugging his fat sides—a glorious feeling. Peanuts walked briskly down the side path, through the side gate, across the road, and down the little lane with no name to Mr. Griffith's house.

Mr. Griffith, a wise and generous old man, was mending a wagon tongue in his shop when I rode up. He kept on working while I told him about Peanuts needing a companion, especially with the chickens gone. He knew about the chickens; everybody did for miles around. I asked him if he had any good ideas about some animal that might do.

He said he didn't right off but would bear it in mind.

Mr. Griffith's bearing something in mind was very good. You could rest on it. I thanked him, nudged Peanuts lightly with my heels, and we started for home.

Halfway down the lane he began to trot, and my hair ribbon bobbed up and down with him, also my stomach and other insides. As we passed under the rose arch, Peanuts saw a tuft of grass, stopped, and leaned down to eat it. To keep from sliding down his long neck, I let go of the rein and grabbed the saddle.

There I sat.

He finished the grass and sauntered across the lawn to more grass by the pine tree. I was powerless to do anything except sit and look toward the house, hoping somebody would see. I was afraid to call

The apple orchard

for help because that might scare him into a bolt. He wandered through the apple orchard, stopping to nibble here and there, nearly knocking me off twice going under low tree limbs.

When he became bored with the orchard, Peanuts crossed the nunnery potato field, newly plowed. Once I almost reached the rein, not quite. He wouldn't hold his head up long enough. Finally we went along a well-worn path through a narrow strip of woods to the ice pond, where a duck came to my rescue.

It was swimming on the pond and Peanuts liked that. He pointed his ears, lifted his head with interest, and the rein slid down his neck right to my hand.

"Get up," I ordered, in power again.

We trotted home.

So, except for the part when Peanuts went where he pleased, my first donkeyback ride was a great success. A few days later, because of it, Mr. Griffith came up with two splendid ideas.

five

BESS

MR. GRIFFITH BROUGHT OVER a crate of chickens for Daddy, a present to take the place of the murdered White Leghorns. They were a job lot—Dominickers, Rhode Island Reds, and one white hen far from a pullet. The rooster, a handsome Dominicker, was nervous. He burst out of the crate the second Mr. Griffith opened the lid and flew around the barnyard squawking and flapping his wings. The hens were even worse. Mr. Kreger threw some cracked corn for them, saying in a high-pitched voice, "Here, chick, chick, chick," and they finally settled down.

As soon as the two men started talking about chicken feed, laying mash, and what to do for the gapes, a disease chickens were apt to get, I went up to the house. A little while later when Mr. Griffith was leaving for home, the empty crates in the back of his wagon, Daddy hailed him from the back porch.

"Whoa, *Mag*," Mr. Griffith said.

The wagon stopped.

I was there swinging in the rope swing on the porch, an excellent swing. You could touch the ceiling with the bottoms of both feet if you were swinging high enough, and I was.

Daddy took his pipe out of his mouth. "Thank you for the chickens, Griffith, thoughtful and generous of you. If there is anything I can do for you at any time you have only to let me know."

Mr. Griffith didn't say anything right away. He was a slow thinker, deep though, and he always thought things out before he spoke, which made what he said worth hearing. And if he didn't have anything to say he kept quiet, which Daddy said was a rare trait.

Mr. Griffith pushed his wide-brimmed hat back on his head so you could see his kind, sunburned face with its droopy white mustache, tobacco stained at the corners.

After a weighty silence he said, "There's a good stand of grass coming in the back field, more than enough for the donkey."

Daddy agreed, drawing on his pipe, a hushed, contented sound.

Mr. Griffith added, leaning forward, "There are plenty of empty stalls in the barn."

Daddy nodded, and I let the swing die down so I wouldn't miss a single word.

Speaking slowly, Mr. Griffith went on, "I was figuring I could bring my cow, Bess, over. In exchange for her board and keep I would milk her night and morning and give Liza half, if you cotton to the idea, Mr. Hayden."

I leaped out of the swing, nearly knocking Daddy flat as I urged him, "Say yes, oh, please say yes, Daddy. Bess would be a perfect friend for Peanuts. She's so peaceful and serene."

Daddy, laugh lines crinkling around his eyes, said that as Mother liked plenty of cream on raspberries maybe it wouldn't be a bad idea.

"Get up, *Mag*."

Mr. Griffith always said Mag louder than anything else he said to her. "I'll bring the cow over first thing in the morning."

He gently slapped the reins across Mag's wide rump and the wagon wheels turned slowly.

Feeling very good about things in general and extremely good about things in particular, I watched the wagon go around the front circle, down the driveway and out the gate. Mag was such a fine, big, warm-hearted horse I wished she *and* Bess were going to live with Peanuts at Nancy's Fancy.

"Ca-thrin," I yelled as loud as I could. I had to tell her the news, and everybody else too. Liza would be so pleased. She had an ice cream freezer way back in the kitchen cupboard on the bottom shelf. Now that we'd have plenty of cream, she'd better get it out, dust it off, and ask Daddy to oil the crank.

Six-thirty the next morning I was sitting alone on the side porch watching for Mr. Griffith and Bess. Catherine was too sleepy to get up. It wasn't long before I saw them, Mr. Griffith leading Bess through the side gate, the milk bucket in his other hand.

I ran down the path to meet them and together we walked to the

The side gate

barn, Bess's full bag swaying gracefully under her big belly.

At the barn I introduced Bess to Peanuts. She was not impressed; cows are that way. She went on chewing her cud, a dreamy look in her large brown eyes. Peanuts was delighted. When I opened the box stall door he shot out, trotted right back, nudged Bess in the side, and blew air on her through his nose. Then, overjoyed, he kicked up his heels and heehawed.

"He's crazy about her, Mr. Griffith," I said, coming out from behind the door. "I don't have a single worry now."

Mr. Griffith laughed, saying it had been a long time since he had been young with no worries. Then he added, "I clean forgot to bring over the milking stool, Nan. Fetch me that box there. It will do for today."

I dragged a wooden ginger ale box from the next stall, first dusting it off with my hand, scaring a black and gold spider.

Mr. Griffith drew the box up close to Bess, sat down, put the bucket under her bag, leaned his head against her side and milked. I sat nearby on a pile of hay, arms around my knees, listening to the swish, swish, swish, of the milk hitting the bucket.

From then on I watched for Mr. Griffith every evening and every morning at milking time. Catherine did not join us regularly, only occasionally as she was not too fond of cows. My sister Ruth liked them a lot, but she was spending the summer at Woods Hole, Massachusetts, studying bugs on a biology scholarship.

One morning Mr. Griffith let me milk one teat, sitting on the little three-legged stool he'd brought over from his house. At first not a drop would come out.

"Squeeze and pull at the same time, Nan," he told me.

When I tried, Bess mooed softly and looked around to see what was going on.

"Not so hard," Mr. Griffith said. "Keep a light, firm hold and pull gently."

A squirt came out and missed the bucket. The next squirt landed in the bucket dead center and Mr. Griffith said, "That's it. Now you've got the combination," and he patted me on the back.

Soon I was milking away, feeling proud, my head pressed hard against Bess's warm side.

It was good to have her at our house. Everybody thought so—
Mother, Daddy, Ruth, Catherine, Mr. Kreger, Liza, and especially
Peanuts. I liked to climb the apple tree, sit on a high limb, and look
down on Peanuts and Bess eating grass together in the field. At first
he tried to make her run so he could chase her and have some fun,
but she wouldn't. He finally gave up and enjoyed her as she was,
contented and not much else.

Then, just when things were so right, everything going along so
fine, a terrible thing happened and it was my fault.

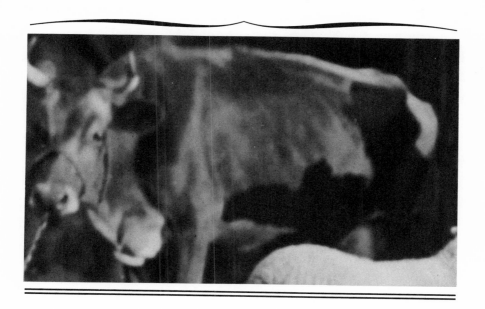

six

THE COW'S TAIL

THE DAY BEFORE the dreadful thing happened, a hot day in August, I spent most of the afternoon waiting for a fat Rhode Island Red to lay an egg. Usually hens tend to the job early but occasionally one like this one is late getting around to it. I stood beside her nest for a long time quiet as anything. Finally she stood up, then sort of crouched down and out it came. While she was cackling, announcing its arrival, I reached my hand under her and felt the egg, warm and firm, perfect in shape. A baby chick would hatch out of it if the hen sat on it long enough—three weeks, so Mr. Griffith said.

Thinking about eggs and baby chicks and the magic of life itself, I walked slowly across the strip of lawn behind Mr. Kreger's house. As I passed the box bush I looked up and was surprised to see Mr. Griffith coming through the side gate with the milk bucket. He never came before five-thirty and I hadn't heard the five o'clock nunnery bell ring.

He was dressed in his best clothes, shoes shined, tie on, white shirt, and a fairly new hat.

"Why so dressed up and why so early?" I asked, skipping beside him on the way to the barn. "Are you going somewhere?"

"I am indeed, Nan," he told me. "My brother and I are going to my sister's house for supper. It's her birthday. We're leaving as soon as the milking's done. In fact, he's sitting on my front porch waiting for me."

I spoke up at once. "You go along home right now. I'll milk tonight. You're too dressed up, and anyway I can do it. A whole cow is only two halves and I've milked half of Bess many times. Leave everything to me this once."

He smiled, showing where a tooth was missing, and said, "That's mighty nice of you, Nan. I know you can do the job as well as I can. When you get done, take the bucket to Liza and ask her to keep my share in the icebox until morning."

"Yes, sir."

Mr. Griffith patted Bess affectionately on her rump, which was bony although the rest of her wasn't, and left the barn walking faster than usual. I heard the barnyard gate click shut and the familiar sound of his footsteps fade to nothing.

Without him the barn seemed extra large and extra quiet. Dust danced along a beam of light coming through a knothole. A fly circled around trying to make up its mind where to land.

As I pulled the milking stool in place I looked across the field toward the woods and there was Peanuts keeping cool in the shade of the trees. I started to milk the two teats nearest to me, swish, swish, working almost as though I were Mr. Griffith. Slowly the bucket began to fill with white foamy milk, and sweat soaked my forehead pressed against Bess.

Buzzzzzzz, buzzzzzzz.

The fly buzzed around my head. I wished it would go away. Instead it landed on Bess's back and sat there preening its wings with its feet until she switched it off with her tail.

Buzzzzzzzzz.

"Oh, go away!"

Buzzzzzzzzzz.

Flip, the cow's tail slapped me in the face.

Sweat trickled down, soaking my blouse.

Buzzzzz.

Flip, the tail slapped me again.

I got up, careful not to upset the bucket, slipped the end of Bess's tail through the latch on the box stall door, and tied a knot with the tassel.

She couldn't swat me now.

I sat down and started to milk again. Two squirts and that pesky fly landed on my knee. *Smack!* I missed it. The fly zinged off and let me finish the milking, which took quite a while—a whole cow is quite a lot.

Finally the job was finished. I dumped oats in Peanuts' manger but did not call him to supper as it was so hot. He'd come in when he wanted to. Mr. Kreger had already fed the chickens. I bade Bess good night and went on up to the kitchen, lugging the almost full bucket.

When I told Liza I had milked Bess all by myself she said she was proud of me. When I boasted about it at dinner the rest of the family was, too, especially Daddy who was not a cow-milking farmer.

He was a specialist at whatever he did outdoors. He planted but did not pick, pruned but didn't clean up the sticks. He was a most beautiful scyther but wouldn't dream of raking hay. Whenever I watched him swing the scythe this way, that way, the rhythm would make me think of Miss Smith standing in front of our class reciting:

> *Break, break, break,*
> *On thy cold gray stones, O sea!*

Daddy said twice—once at dinner and again later—that milking a cow was a real accomplishment.

The next morning when Mr. Griffith came to milk, the light in the stable was dim. Neither one of us noticed the cow's tail still tied to the door latch.

He milked expertly, swiftly, telling me through his mustache about the birthday dinner at his sister's. I leaned against the post behind him, listening, chewing on a straw that tasted sweet. The job finished, Mr. Griffith pushed back the stool, slapped Bess gently and said, "That's all for now, Old Girl. Run along and eat some grass."

She turned and ran out.

Poor, poor Bess. There was a cracking sound, a low moan, and there hanging on the latch was the end of her tail, the long tassel and at least three inches of meat and bone.

I had to get away somewhere and hide. There was no use crying because tears could never wash away my cruelty, my thoughtless terrible cruelty.

I ran to the house fast, crossed the back porch, and went in the ice-man's pantry door. I went straight to the back pantry next to Daddy's indoor shop and hid under the bottom shelf that was full of empty preserving jars.

I didn't deserve to have any animals, not now or ever, not even Peanuts. I suffered all over—bones, flesh, and insides.

After a long time I heard the pantry door open, the one to the dining room, and Liza came in. She must have sensed something was wrong, for she came right to the back pantry, looked in and said, "What in the world are you doing down there with the pickle crock, Miss Nan?"

I burst into tears and told her what had happened. She tried to comfort me, saying I shouldn't take it so to heart, I hadn't meant to hurt Bess. Mother and Catherine said the same thing. Daddy didn't. His never-to-be-forgotten eyes judged me.

I almost wished he'd spank me but I knew he wouldn't.

Right then I would have welcomed the Queen of Hearts' "Off with her head," I needed to be punished so. And I was. Seven mornings and seven evenings Mr. Griffith came through the side gate and cut across the lower cornfield without even looking toward the house. He brought our share of milk to Liza at the back door and went on down the path without even a nod to me sitting on the side porch, miserable beyond miserable.

Eight days, nine days. He did not take Bess away, though I wouldn't have blamed him if he had.

I did not go near the barn, could not, for fear of seeing what was left of Bess's tail. I couldn't even feed Peanuts. Catherine fed him for me. Then, on the tenth morning, Mr. Griffith called out to me on the way to the barn, "Want to help with the milking, Nan?"

Did I want to! More than anything, even at the risk of seeing the tail. I walked beside him not saying anything, looking at my feet.

There, waiting for us at the barnyard gate stood Bess—with a perfectly good, full-length tail! Complete with a tassel on the end.

I looked up at Mr. Griffith and he said, "It's the selfsame tail, Nan, nearly as good as new. *You* ran. I stayed and did what I could. I greased the stump, put the torn part in place, bone to bone, and bound it with cloth soaked in tar. It's growing together again real good."

Tears of joy blinded me as I hugged Bess, getting a horn hooked in my hair ribbon.

"Never run away from things, Nan," Mr. Griffith told me while he was milking. "No matter what, stay and face it. That is the *only* way to live, child, the only worthwhile way to live."

I promised him I would never run away from anything ever again.

seven

A VERY FULL WEEK

MOTHER WAS GOING TO SWARTHMORE to visit her sister, our Aunt Tat. As soon as I heard the news, I began to miss her even before she left. Catherine and I helped her pack, and then, on Monday morning, we watched her get on the streetcar, ride around the bend and out of sight.

We went into the kitchen for comfort.

"I'm here to look after you children," Liza told us, not looking up from kneading dough on the breadboard. "And Grandma and Auntie will be along in time for lunch and stay until your mother gets back home."

"We know that," Catherine declared. "It's their vacation and we promised Mother we'd do our best to entertain them while they're here."

"I can't do a thing about it on Wednesday, don't forget," I said, feeling important. "I'm going to spend the night at Robbins' house. Mother said I could."

Liza nodded her bent-down head, kneading the dough with both hands, tucking it in and kneading it again. Catherine said she hadn't forgotten I was going, and as I was, we'd better line up some things right away and not waste time.

Grandma and Auntie arrived on the eleven-fifteen, each carrying a plump black satchel, Auntie a cretonne bag in her other hand. We were glad to see them, really glad. I said so twice to Catherine and she said so once to me. We would show them a good time for three reasons: because Mother had asked us to, because we wanted to, and because it would be more fun than moping around wishing Mother would hurry up and come on home where she belonged.

Right after lunch we hitched Peanuts to the donkey cart. He was pretty steady now after several trial runs with Daddy. We drove around the house and stopped by the front porch where Grandma and Auntie were sewing.

"Who wants to take a ride?" I asked cheerfully, leaning over the front of the basket edge of the cart and patting Peanuts on the rump.

Grandma didn't. Neither did Auntie at first. After Catherine said, "Oh, come on, Auntie. It's lots of fun," she laid her white fluff of sewing on the green chair and joined us. As she stepped into the cart Grandma cautioned, "Do be careful, Caroline."

"Yes, Mother."

"Get up, Peanuts."

We drove up the lane as far as Johnny Cake Road and back, about two miles each way. Peanuts trotted enough to keep us awake and galloped when the ice wagon tried to pass us, the big horse snorting through his nose close behind us, his big hoofs clopping on a much lower note than Peanuts'. Aside from that, the ride was uneventful. Still it was an important ride. As we bobbed along, Auntie's eyes lost their left-out look, her hair fluffed out, pink crept under the skin on her cheeks, and her mouth softened and turned up slightly at the corners.

"Auntie had a good time, didn't she?" I said as we unhitched.

Catherine nodded yes, then said, "I wish we could think of some way to entertain Grandma."

"I do, too. How about giving a play for her?"

"Good idea. We'll work it up and give it tomorrow in the barn." There was the crunch of bicycle wheels behind us. "Oh, hi, Will," Catherine said, turning around, "you're just in time."

"To do what?" Will hopped off his bicycle and scratched his skinny left ankle at the same time, which was not easy to do.

"Ride around and tell everybody to come over early tomorrow to practice a play we're going to give at three o'clock."

"Who's going to be in it?" Will asked and Catherine told him, "Everybody. Hand me the currycomb, Nan."

"If everybody's in it, who will see it?"

Currying the stick-me-tights off of Peanuts' coat, Catherine answered sharply, "You're worse than Gladys, asking silly questions. Grandma and Auntie, Mr. Griffith, Mr. Kreger maybe, and anybody's relatives can come. Three o'clock tomorrow."

Catherine and me

"Free?"

"Of course, Will. You know Daddy doesn't approve of children making money." She combed away vigorously and Will hopped on his bike and pushed off.

We gave Peanuts a bucket of water and turned him loose in the field. Then we walked back to the house and formally invited Grandma and Auntie to the play. They accepted formally.

After that, until dinner time, and from after dinner until late that night, Catherine and I drummed up the play.

It was a good play, really dramatic. Actors arrived at seven-thirty A.M., the audience at two forty-five: Gladys's mother and father; Landon's mother, baby sister, nurse, and chauffeur, and older brother Jack; Mr. Griffith and his next door neighbor; everybody for miles around except Liza who would not leave the house.

Grandma had the best seat, a kitchen chair placed in the middle of the open big doors of the barn where she could see perfectly. At the most exciting part of Act 2, Billy, taking the part of a sea captain, the wicked villain, was choking Catherine, the heroine, at the ship's rail, the edge of the hayloft. At the crucial moment Catherine ducked out of sight in the loft and David pushed a dummy Catherine in her place, a dress of hers stuffed with hay, stuffed stockings pinned to the hem. The villain shook the dummy unmercifully, Catherine screaming in the background. Next, with a blood-curdling yell he tossed the dummy overboard. It landed with a loud thud right at Grandma's feet.

Startled, she reared back quite the way Peanuts did when he was startled, and keeled over—black silk, watch pin, rings, pompadour, and all. Everyone rushed to her at once, thinking she had fainted. She hadn't, though; the left back leg of the kitchen chair had just buckled under.

As we all tried to help her to her feet, cast and audience, she waved us aside, saying to a tearful Auntie, "Give me your hand, Caroline, and do try to cheer up. I am perfectly all right." She drank some water Bill offered her in Mr. Kreger's tin cup and I couldn't help wondering where he got it—Peanuts' bucket? Bess's? Not the chickens' water, I hoped.

Mr. Kreger, without being told, which I thought was remarkable considering, fetched the solid-as-a-rock green Windsor chair from the front porch and set it behind Grandma. She thanked him, sat down and composed herself, pushing a few loose hairpins in place. Then she looked straight at us children lined up in front of her.

"Well, aren't we ever going to see the rest of the play?"

Never had I felt a closer bond with Grandma and Auntie.

At the end of Act 3, the last act, the applause was loud and enthusiastic. More so after Catherine's bow alone, still more for Catherine and the villain. And when the whole cast bowed, Peanuts hurried up from the back field curious about what was going on in the uphill side of his barn.

The next day was Wednesday. All set to leave for Robbins' house in a navy dotted Swiss dress and navy hair ribbon, and with a nightgown and a change of underwear in the cretonne knitting bag borrowed from Auntie, I called from the porch, "Ca-thrin!"

She came at once and, shaking a finger to make her notice every word, I told her, "Be sure Peanuts has water all the time, and if you tie him out while I'm gone, be sure he has both water and shade."

By way of an answer she smiled at me, head on the side, hands behind her—a girl to leave your donkey with if ever I saw one.

"Good-bye, everybody. See you tomorrow."

I ran down the driveway swinging the knitting bag in wide circles, wishing Mother were home to wave to me. I caught the two o'clock streetcar, walked fast down Ingleside past St. Timothy's Church, crossed Frederick Road, passed the school, and on down Bloomsbury Avenue. Robbins' house, high and square, sat between another much like it and the German orphanage.

Robbins was waiting for me on the steps. She had a pink dress on and didn't look one speck like the pitcher on the soft ball team, county champion speed runner, and captain of the dodge ball team, which she was.

"Hi, Nan," she said as I ran up the path taking an occasional leap. "I thought you'd never get here. Put your things down and let's play hopscotch. I've already drawn the lines on the road at the side of the house and I found us these two flat stones. Aren't they peachy?"

She handed me a stone and we began to play. That's the one thing I liked about Robbins, you didn't waste time with her.

As we were an even match, the game was fun. She won the first, I won the second. After tying the third we sat on the steps to rest, hot and happy. After a while Robbins leaned forward and drew a funny face in the dirt at her feet with the edge of her stone, her curls falling in front. "Nan," she said, "we've been best friends for years, haven't we?"

"Since the day we met in Mother's baby class at Sunday school when we were three."

We giggled over that and she said, "We'll be friends forever." I nodded and she went on, "Let's do something about it. Want to?"

"What?"

"I don't know. We could bury our stones side by side some place."

"Good idea. Where?"

"Let's find a place. Come on."

I followed her down the path to the sidewalk and she pointed to a brick, third one from the curb, right in front of her gate.

I nodded and we got busy. We pried the brick up with a kitchen knife, laid our two flat stones side by side on the damp earth, pressed them down hard, and put the brick back in place. We shook hands over the stones, saying together, "Forever," and the ceremony was over.

Forever our stones would be there. Forever we would be best friends.

Supper was almost a party, with a fancy dessert. Games were fun in the evening. Later on, though, was not fun. I was used to my soft quiet sister sleeping beside me. Robbins had elbows sharp as arrowheads and she twisted and turned in her sleep. Twice she gritted her teeth.

Lying there wide awake in the dark in a strange room, I began to think I was getting a stiff neck. I felt it all around and up under my ears with my fingers. No, it wasn't sore at all. I was imagining things. Some nights will do that to you even at home, when the wind is blowing and the moon not out.

eight

MOSTLY ABOUT DOGS AND CATS

THE FOLLOWING THURSDAY afternoon Grandma was sewing in the gray chair on the porch. Mother, home again, was retouching prints in the green chair, and Auntie was rocking in the rocking chair, her sensible black shoes squeaking in time with the rockers. Daddy was at the office, Ruth still at Woods Hole, Mr. Kreger hilling up the celery bed. Catherine and I were out in the kitchen helping Liza shell lima beans for succotash.

There was a screeching of automobile brakes down on Edmondson Avenue near the side gate, then the sound of the auto racing away. I jumped up, spilling a lapful of beans on the brick hearth. Catherine stepped in the colander as the two of us hurried to the window to see what was going on. Little Jack raced up the side path and behind him Bob struggled to walk. Under the rose arch he staggered and dropped over on his side.

"He's been hurt!" Catherine exclaimed, and we ran out the back door, around the house and down the path as fast as we could.

Bob was lying there, still, not moving at all. We leaned over him, afraid to touch him. There was not a mark to show where the automobile hit him, but we knew it had and we knew he was dead.

We cried and cried, tears dropping on his handsome coat.

Still crying, we ran to the house. "He tried to get to us before he died," sobbed Catherine after we'd told the sad news. Mother almost cried with us and we got louder and louder.

I could tell through my tears that Grandma and Auntie did not approve of the way we were handling our sorrow. I don't mean they weren't sorry. They were, very sorry, only they believed in control when possible. I did, too, but at that moment it just wasn't.

Liza must have told Mr. Kreger about the accident or else he saw it himself because he went down the side path pushing the wheelbarrow. I didn't look after that. The thought of Bob's lovely plume tail hanging lifeless over the side of the wheelbarrow was more than I could stand.

At five-thirty Daddy came home. He did not say a word when Mother told him about Bob except to ask if Mr. Kreger had taken care of the body. Still, you could feel his sorrow and you knew that Bob would always be part of him. Daddy would never go to pieces no matter what. If everything he believed in fell apart, he'd stand and build it up again. Only you can't build people or dogs or trees or anything that lives once they are dead.

I wanted to tell Daddy how sorry I was but I couldn't, so I wrote a note—"Dear Daddy, I am sorry"—and put it by his chair in the living room. Catherine hugged him, which he liked. Life is simpler for huggers, I believe, much simpler than for non-huggers.

Jack took his grief under the kitchen table. There was nothing for him or us to do but go on living without Bob, so that is what we did.

One day when new grass was just beginning to come up on Bob's grave, a pretty place under the walnut tree outside the barnyard, Mother called, "Nan, would you like to see if the mail has come?" Except in emergencies Mother never gave an order—do this, do that; she asked if you wanted to do something.

As I was only practicing jacks on the side porch, I put the ball in my middy blouse pocket and skipped down the side path to the

Jack, posing for us in the front driveway

mailbox, a wooden homemade box nailed to the gatepost.

I lifted the lid and nobody could ever have guessed what was in-side—a mother cat and five adorable kittens, one black with white paws, two plain gray, and two faintly striped. They were cute enough to balance all the sorrow in the world.

I closed the lid, careful not to come down on a tail or a whisker, and ran up the path shouting the news.

Nobody else was pleased, not even Catherine. Mother raised her eyebrows and said, "So many?" Liza, looking out the front door, said, "Five kittens *and* a mother cat?" Mr. Kreger laughed, "He, he," scratching himself with the short-handled trowel.

Catherine said she didn't see how anybody could be mean enough to desert a whole family of cats, but she helped me bring them up to the house in the clothesbasket and fix a box for them in the cellar.

Daddy took it the hardest. He set his book down with a bang, left it there on the table for a full minute before he picked it up again.

Later on, when the kittens were chasing their tails and each other on the lawn, people loosened up some. We called the mother cat Kitty, the kittens, Blackie, Susan, Dorian, Babe. The littlest one we named Mullikin after Anna Mullikin, Ruth's best friend, a deli-cately pretty young woman who was almost as good at mathematics as Daddy.

It was because of mathematics that I gave up the cats.

I sat in the swing on the front porch, not a bit happy. Daddy stood in front of me and said, "If one cat produces five kittens every three months in one year there would be twenty kittens. Right?"

Me, with Jack and the mother cat

I nodded, although I did not like to multiply kittens by months.

He went on. "For the record let us assume that two and a half of the original kittens are female."

"Two and a *half* kittens!" This was going too far.

He leaned down, knocked the ashes out of his pipe on the edge of the porch, and said, "Let me put it another way in simple logic. Your mother likes birds, we all do. Cats catch birds. Therefore the cats must live elsewhere."

"Mr. Griffith says it's built into a cat to catch birds, they aren't being mean," I said weakly, knowing I'd lost the case.

The dinner bell rang and I followed Daddy gloomily to the dining room. During rice pudding I said, "One thing for sure, we've got to find a good home for every single cat—a *good* home, not just any old place."

Everybody agreed to that and I pushed back my chair saying, "Come on, Catherine, we might as well get going."

We hitched Peanuts to the cart and started out with Susan, Blackie, Dorian, and Babe in a hatbox, air holes punched in the lid. While Catherine held the box on her lap so we wouldn't spill kittens, I drove. Now and then I'd see a paw playfully clawing at one of the holes.

and a neighbor's dog

We drove over to Dot's house first and had the best luck. Dot's grandmother took Babe. At the next stop, Gladys's, we had no luck. And none at Billy's, David's, or the seven houses on North Bend Road, either.

We went home discouraged and we stayed discouraged until the next meeting of the Friendly Aid Society at St. Timothy's Church. While the Friendly Aiders were sewing for the unfortunate, Mother persuaded two of them to adopt Blackie and Dorian.

A teacher at Auntie's school promised to give Susan a good home. Auntie took her to town in a box and said she only meowed once.

By this time I fully agreed with Daddy that twenty kittens would be impossible. And we still had the mother cat and Mullikin on our hands. They were my favorites. I talked them up so much to Mr. Griffith that he gave in and took them home with him. I was so glad. Anybody, cat or not, would like to live with Mr. Griffith.

Nancy's Fancy was empty without Bob and all the cats, but it didn't stay empty long. Ruth came home from Woods Hole looking sunburned and marvelous, and brought with her two other biology majors from New York, young men, twins, exactly alike, fun and talented. They played the piano together, one the left hand, the other the right, singing in close harmony, heads together, "Come on and hear, come on and hear, Alexander's Rag Time Band," a new song that made you want to dance.

The twins stayed two days and nights, rode Peanuts bareback, climbed trees, played tennis, sang, laughed, and ate, ate, ate. The day they left, school started. We had Miss Smith for another year. She moved up to the fourth grade with us and we were glad, all of us, which certainly was a compliment to her.

Ruth,
looking marvelous

The first day back, as I went into the basement of the school to leave my bicycle, I saw a dog hanging around the outside door. A real friendly, tail-wagging, middle-sized plain brown dog, with traces of boxer here and there or maybe it was bulldog. I gave him part of a ham sandwich, patted him on the head, and the next day he was there and the next and the next. Friday he was still hanging around. There wouldn't be anybody to feed him or give him water until Monday.

"Here, boy, come on. I'll take you home with me," I said as I pushed my bike out of the bike stand.

He sat down and looked at me.

I put my book strap around his neck for a collar and pulled him along, balancing the bicycle as well as I could with my left hand.

The dog didn't help at all. It took me ages to drag him across Ingleside Avenue. To speed things, I took off my hair ribbon, tied one end of it to the strap, the other end to the luggage carrier, and got on my bike. It didn't work.

By the time I'd dragged him bodily down the first long hill I was worn out and so was he. Almost in tears I set him free. Then without once looking back I rode the rest of the way home, fast.

I swerved through the side gate, stood up on the pedals to pump hard going up the path, and hopped off at the back door. There, right behind me was the brown dog, panting, wagging his tail, pleased as anything.

He and Daddy hit it off fine at once. Daddy named him Brutus. From that day on Brutus slept under the kitchen table with Jack. Although he didn't take Bob's place, no dog could, he made an important place of his own.

I'd hoped he would be my dog but he chose to be Daddy's.

DONKEYBACK TO SCHOOL AND THE PEABODY DANCERS

USUALLY I WAS OUT OF BED the second Liza called from downstairs, but one morning I overslept. I didn't hear a thing until she called again, adding, "You'd better fly, Miss Nan, or you'll be late for school! Your father's frowning at your empty chair."

I leaped out of bed and in two shakes of a pig's tail was on the way downstairs, dress unbuttoned, shoestrings flapping.

"Sorry I'm late, Daddy. I didn't hear a thing until just now. Oh, boy, hot cakes!" I slid into my chair, reaching for the little squat syrup pitcher with the bent nose.

Ruth, sitting across the table, hair on top of her head like a grown woman, said, "Hey—you forgot to wash your face." She lifted her glass of water, eyes bright and devilish. "Dare me to wash it for you?"

"Double dare you," I said with a mouth full, sure she wouldn't.

Water sailed across the table and sloshed me in the face, soaked my blouse and skirt, diluted the syrup on my stack of pancakes, spattered on the floor.

Catherine giggled. Daddy pushed back his chair and with an "Excuse me, Emily!" left the table, the morning paper under his arm. And Mother said, "Ruth, how could you?"

"Don't blame me," Ruth said, tucking a stray curl in place at the nape of her neck, both rounded arms raised. "It was Nan's fault. She dared me."

"Double dared you," put in Catherine, out of character. She practically always stuck up for me.

Mother laid her napkin on the table, saying, "Nan, go change into dry clothes and be quick about it," then hurried to say good-bye to Daddy.

Catherine waited for me to get dressed but she had to go to school without me because my back tire was flat, a slow leak in the valve, and we couldn't find the pump anywhere.

By the time Mother found two nickels for carfare I'd missed the eight-thirty streetcar and the next one would make me late for school.

I sat on the front step, knees hunched up, chin in my hands. Late for breakfast and now late for school and I hated to be late.

Ruth came to the door behind me and said, "Why don't you ride the donkey? I'll saddle him for you." Sort of making up for washing my face, I guessed, as she was not the let-me-do-it-for-you type that Catherine was. She was marvelous, though. Besides being lightning smart, very popular, and extremely pretty, she cared about what happened to the whole world and I was sure she would do something about it some day. I wanted to be just like her, but Liza said I never would because Ruth was tender sometimes, sensible always, and I was just tender.

Anyway, riding donkeyback to school was a great idea. Mother said I could this once if I kept over to the side of the road. While Ruth saddled up, she called Mr. Davis at the feed store and asked if it was all right for me to leave Peanuts tied to his hitching post. He said it was.

In no time Peanuts was trotting up Edmondson Avenue with me in the saddle, my books and lunch strapped across the front. He was in a brisk but level-headed mood. Near Ingleside Avenue an automobile passed us making a racket and it didn't even bother him. I was proud to ride him any place now and doubly proud to ride him to school where everybody could see him.

While I was tying him to the hitching post in Mr. Davis's shed, Mr. Davis came along and said, "I'll water the donkey for you when he cools down, Nan."

I thanked him, patted Peanuts' nose, and took a short cut across the school lawn, books under one arm, lunch under the other, ribbon sliding off, skirt rumpled.

Opening exercises were in full swing as I came into our room, everybody standing, saluting the flag, reciting in unison, "one nation, indivisible, with liberty and justice for all."

After the scramble of feet, people sitting down, I said, "I had a flat tire, Miss Smith, missed the streetcar, and if I hadn't ridden donkeyback I wouldn't be here now."

A giggle ran around the room. For some reason just to mention a donkey was funny to some people—not to me or Miss Smith, though. She said, "Get out your arithmetic books, children, and turn to page nine."

Mixed with the sounds of desk tops slamming, books landing on desks, pages being ruffled, was a pitiful braying that floated through the open window, "Oink-eeee, oink-eeee, oink-eee."

"He's calling me," I said, and the rest of the class burst out laughing.

Miss Smith clapped her hands for attention and one of the boys in the back of the room said, "Heehaw," which even I thought was funny. Then Peanuts brayed again in a high annoyed tone and somebody up front did, too.

Poor Miss Smith. She rapped on her desk with a ruler and said, "The next one to bray will be sent to the principal's office."

"Oink-eee, oink-eee," brayed Peanuts and the class roared. Miss Smith gave up and joined in on one of the biggest all-out laughs our class ever had.

Peanuts kept calling me, not continually, just enough to keep us from getting much work done. Evidently our class was not the only one disrupted. Around eleven o'clock a sixth-grader brought a note to Miss Smith from the principal's office suggesting that she send me home for the rest of the day and not to mark me absent.

So Peanuts and I left. As we galloped past school, his tail flying, every window was full of laughing faces and waving hands and loud imitation heehaws filled the air.

Instead of going across Ingleside and down Edmondson Avenue, we went home the other way, down Frederick Road and up Nunnery Lane to Edmondson. I intended to go through the side gate but couldn't; a delivery wagon was blocking the way. So I headed Peanuts for the front gate.

We hadn't gone five steps when I suddenly stopped Peanuts, my mouth wide open in surprise. Wagons, buggies, automobiles, were lined up all along the edge of the lawn: Griffith's and Turner's, the John S. Wilson Company milk wagons, horses nibbling on the grass, drivers standing beside them, backs toward the road. Even Catonsville's new fire engine, a beautiful red motor engine the envy of ten towns around, was there, the hook and ladder taking up a block-long space.

What in the world was going on?

Peanuts, as interested and curious as I was, held his head high, ears pointed as he skirted around the red flag sticking way out behind the hook and ladder and turned in the front gate.

Now I could see. Mother was taking pictures. Her camera was set up in the middle of the lawn, the lens aimed at a bevy of dancers in diaphanous gowns. I drew rein near the hitching post on the circle and sat in the saddle to watch.

"Once more, girls," Mother called out, coming from under the black headcloth, her hair net hanging down her back. "This time dance in front of the pine tree and stop when I say to. Ready, go!"

The young women from the Peabody Institute in Baltimore

danced across the lawn, bare feet, bare legs, flimsy chiffon gowns, hair blowing, wispy veils floating behind them.

"Hold it, hold it!"

They stopped and held a beautiful pose. Mother squeezed the camera bulb. "That was fine, girls," she said, and she wiped her forehead with one of Daddy's large handkerchiefs, she was working so hard.

The dancers danced on around the tree for the fun of it, to the delight of the crowd gathered on the edge of the lawn. Drivers from the parked wagons and automobiles, the postman, and two strangers on foot clapped and cheered. The iceman gave a shrill whistle of appreciation.

Mr. Kreger, leaning on the rake handle by the peony bed, was too entranced to applaud.

Nobody noticed Peanuts and me, not even Liza, who was watching the show from the side porch.

Mother, the black headcloth tucked in her belt, hurried over to the trumpet vine where she set up the camera for the next picture.

"In this one, girls," she said, "face the camera, veils overhead and knees high this way." She danced, the black cloth waving in the air.

The Peabody dancers and I laughed, Mother was so funny. Nobody else did. Their full attention was on the girls' legs, or limbs as Grandma preferred us to say.

Limbs were rare. Even in long black stockings they were seen only at the seashore, except for an ankle now and then when a skirt

swung or was lifted slightly at a doorsill or a puddle.

I watched Mother take the front-view picture and heard her say with enthusiasm, "Splendid! Just what I wanted."

As she cleaned her steamed-up glasses on her white shirttail, the dancers gathered around her. People always did. Mother drew them to her like a magnet and held them with her wit and quick-moving conversation.

"We'd better take one more of that same pose, girls," she said, "just in case somebody moved and spoiled the plate."

The dancers ran across the lawn, talking and laughing. Peanuts and I went down to the barn to unsaddle.

The photographs of the Peabody dancers turned out to be very good. To me, though, they were not as good as my three favorites— Mother listening to Ruth, taken when Ruth was a little girl; a full face bust portrait of Peanuts; and Ruth as Mr. Pickwick wearing Daddy's long winter underwear stuffed to give her the right shape.

ten

THE BISHOP

FALL FLEW BY, so much going on at school, with Thanksgiving to top it off. December was full and fast: school play on the seventeenth, Mother's birthday the twentieth, Liza's birthday, Christmas Eve, Christmas itself and the holidays, Ruth home from college, the house full of people, fun, new things, and lots of goodies. Then New Year's and back to school again.

Wednesday, the second week in January, a bishop was coming to have his picture taken. He'd seen Mother's bust portrait of Peanuts, a beautiful soft platinum print, in a photographic exhibition at the Baltimore Museum of Art and he wanted one just like it of himself.

So the date for the sitting was set and we were excited.

Because of the weather the sitting was postponed. It had to be, for that Tuesday it snowed all night and by morning the world was beautiful and new. Mother was out right after breakfast with her boots on, skirt tucked into Daddy's pants, stocking cap pulled down over her ears, lugging the long-legged camera. Everything posed for its picture except the Bishop: the gatepost, the dipping limb of the catalpa tree, Mr. Kreger's house, the barn, the pine trees all trimmed in white.

Jack and Brutus ran around in circles, sending up clouds of feathery snow. I wished for Bob. He would have loved it. Peanuts looked over the barnyard fence and heehawed for breakfast. As Mr. Kreger was clearing a path to the streetcar for Daddy, Catherine and I shoveled right and left like a couple of snowplows making a path to the barn.

The snow was deep, too deep for a bishop, too deep for sledding. The next day was perfect for both but the Bishop couldn't come until the following Wednesday.

Although we were disappointed about him, we made the most of the sledding. David, Howard, Billy, and the rest of us pulled our sleds to the top of Nunnery Lane and skimmed down the long hill fast, the cold wind taking our breath away. It was positively great, snow hard-packed, ice in the ruts. We stayed out until nearly dark and went home, hands and feet frozen, noses red.

The next day sledding was not very good on the road but it was excellent on our hill by the barn. We made a snowman on the lawn and a fort by the barnyard fence where Peanuts and Bess could see us.

Nancy's Fancy in winter

The boys wanted to hitch Peanuts to our big Flexible Flyer, but I wouldn't let them. I was afraid he might slip and break a leg. Horses with broken legs had to be shot, I'd heard, and I wasn't taking any chances. Still, when Ruth's friends Adelle and Ray Gildia went by in their sleigh, the horse stepping high, sleigh bells ringing, I was tempted.

Snow made the week go by fast. Before we knew it, it was Wednesday, the day of the Bishop's sitting, this time for sure.

I sneezed twice during breakfast. Because I very much wanted to see the Bishop who was coming at three, I said maybe it would be a good idea to stay home and get a jump on my cold before it started. Mother thought that was a sensible idea.

It was fun being home with Mother, having her all to myself. Lunchtime was especially nice, just the two of us, the silver teapot, and the soup tureen. Liza had started a fire in the dining room fireplace. It popped now and then, the wood falling down and needing to be poked. An oil painting of Mother's grandmother hung over the mantel, her eyes looking down at us from under a frilled lace cap.

"Will the Bishop have on his costume when he gets here, Mother?" I asked when I was halfway finished with my second bowl of homemade vegetable soup.

"Vestments, dear, not costume," Mother said. "No, he will be wearing a business suit and change into vestments in the studio."

I went on scooping up soup, thinking to myself that it would be interesting to watch a bishop put on vestments to see what went on top of what.

Ministers I knew quite well. Ours at St. Timothy's, Mr. Yardley, was such a close friend he said if he took his hands off the wheel of his automobile it would turn in our gate by itself. He was a scholar in the pulpit, so Mother said. Out of the pulpit he was a splendid game player—checkers, halma, chess, any kind of game. However, I did not know a bishop firsthand.

Catherine and Ruth did because they had been confirmed. I had not, to the distress of Grandma and Auntie, because Mother and Daddy thought a person should reach some degree of maturity first.

Around ten minutes of three I went upstairs to the studio, the second-floor front room across the landing from Ruth's room. The camera was set up in front of an armchair. Behind the chair there was a muted green screen, a background for the Bishop.

I went into the clothes closet and sat down on the floor behind the two-piece tapestry curtain which served as the door. It seemed all right to at the time, though later I realized it wasn't. Over my head hung costumes that Mother posed people in. Near my nose was a faded brown lawn dress, Empire style, that Ruth's friend Anna had worn in the picture of her standing in front of Mr. Kreger's house with one of the kittens in her arms. My grandmother's wedding dress was there, a beautiful stiff satin with braid on the wide sleeves and around the extremely low neck. Ada Shuter, soprano soloist at St. Timothy's and cherry-picking friend, wore it in the exhibition picture of her and Brutus in front of the parlor fireplace. A plum-colored shawl, fringed all the way around, was beside it, and next was my favorite, a white dimity dress, old, fragile, lovely as a moth wing.

There is not much to do while you wait in a closet for a bishop except to wish he'd hurry and get there. To amuse myself, I ran my finger along a crack between two boards under my humped-up knees and found a candy left from Christmas, a dusty striped peppermint. It wasn't too bad. Every Christmas Mother turned the studio over to us so we could play there with our friends all the time and not have to put things away.

I wished for Robbins. She would be fine to wait for a bishop with and to watch one get dresesd with, too. I didn't wish for Catherine as I wasn't sure she'd approve.

Before long I heard an automobile come up the driveway and

stop out front. I heard Mother greet the Bishop in the hall and visit with him for a few minutes in the parlor. Out in the hall again I heard Mother say, "The studio is on the left, the second landing. Call me when you are ready to pose."

Heavy, measured footsteps came up to the first landing and on up the five more steps to the next.

I leaned forward and parted the curtain an inch so I could see the Bishop come in. He set a large black suitcase down under the window and took off his black suit coat, which he hung on the back of a chair. He stood there in shirt sleeves, sort of a bib, and a white round collar. After a few moments he scratched his head vigorously with all ten fingers. Then he hiked up his pants to give his knees more room and stooped down. After scratching the middle of his back with five fingers only, he opened the suitcase.

He rummaged around in it for a few minutes then said aloud, "Damn that woman! She forgot to put in my red chimere."

Well! A *bishop* swearing! The *very idea.* With as much indignation as I could muster, I flung open the curtains, saying, "I heard what you said. You swore and you ought to be ashamed." It was the shock that made me so bold. Without it I never in the world would have spoken out that way to a bishop, a minister, a teacher, or any other grown person.

He stood up, furious, red-faced, and glared at me.

"What are you doing in there? Come out at once. *You* are the one who should be ashamed, hiding in there, spying on me."

"*I* am not a bishop," I declared, getting to my feet and stumbling awkwardly into the room.

"True, true." He nodded his handsome head. "You are one up

on me there." Then in a deep, reverberating voice, the one he used
for blessing people I was sure, he added, "I am sorry for my fall from
grace and shall strive diligently never to do so again."

He meant it.

"And I am sorry I hid. I wanted to see how you put on your
vestments. I'll never do such a thing again, either. It was sneaky
and I hate sneaks."

I meant it too.

Looking up at him, I said, "I hope you won't tell on me."

His eyes took on the same look as Ruth's when she was winning
at checkers. "I won't tell on you if you don't tell on me."

"I won't tell, I promise."

"Good."

A warm smile spread over his face. We shook hands and I went
on downstairs and out to the kitchen. He invited me to stay and
watch him dress but I declined politely. I might never know what
went on top of what, but I knew a bishop face to face and he knew
me.

Several of the photographs turned out fine. I saw the one he chose
himself while it was wet, lying on a folded white sheet on the back
room floor. The bishop was not quite as handsome as Peanuts. Almost though, and the expression around the eyes was similar.

eleven

DEE GEE

"MISS CATHERINE! MISS NAN!" Liza called from the house.

We were in the barn, uphill part, the big doors propped wide open. Will and David were there helping us make a speed wagon out of two long boards and the wheels off of Dot's broken-down stroller. We had worked hard all day and by the middle of the afternoon the wagon was in pretty good shape, wheels on, and Catherine was trying to drill a hole for the fancy steering gear the boys invented.

Liza called again and my sister said, "Go and see what she wants, Nan. I'm busy."

I was busy too, but I handed the screwdriver to Will and ran as

far as the cherry tree. "What do you want, Liza?" I yelled. I could
see her white apron and white head handkerchief in the dark kitchen
doorway.

"Mr. Cline is here."

"On a weekday afternoon? Are you sure, Liza?" I asked, running
closer. School was closed for an all-day teachers' meeting.

"Didn't I tell you he's here? I saw him drive through the gate
a few minutes ago, that black horse of his stepping high. I watched
him hitch the horse to the post on the circle and came to tell you
children."

"Mrs. Cline, too?"

"Just him."

Mr. Cline was Daddy's best friend and a favorite of the whole
family. Mother said we mustn't forget Mrs. Cline. She was real nice,
only when he was there you didn't notice her or anybody else.

Mr. Cline had a bald head, or almost bald, and a fat middle. He
always wore a pressed suit, a white shirt, and expensive tie. He had
small neat feet and hands and the biggest laugh in the world.

When the Clines came to dinner and stayed late, after Catherine
and I were supposed to be in bed we'd sit on the top step in the
hall, nightgowns on, feet bare, to hear Mr. Cline laugh down in the
living room. He was bound to if you waited long enough, and when
he did we'd throw back our heads and laugh with him. You had to.

As Mr. Cline never came to see us on a weekday afternoon, I had
to find out why he was here. I ran along the brick path beside the
house and around front. He was standing by the step, talking to
Mother and in his arms was a little white lamb.

"Where did you get it, Mr. Cline? Whose is it? May I hold it?"

I asked, all in one breath.

Mr. Cline laughed. "It's yours, Nan, if you like it."

Like it? I was wild about it. I took the baby lamb in my arms and hugged it, so soft and warm. Its slender legs hung down limp, tipped with hoofs no bigger than my thumb.

"Maa-aaa," it said, and Mother said to Mr. Cline, "Maybe we should ask Charles before deciding about the lamb, Frank."

I was about to say no to that when Mr. Cline settled the question by saying, "I was over at the slaughterhouse on business this morning and saw the lamb, born during the night while its mother was waiting to be slaughtered. It was such a pretty little thing I thought Nan might like to raise it."

"Yes," was all I could say, my mind too full of the cruel scene. As soon as I could collect my thoughts and clear away the ones I couldn't bear, I added, "Thank you, Mr. Cline. I'm going to show her to Catherine and Liza. Please give my regards to your horse."

With the lamb in my arms, her little head resting against my shoulder, I walked slowly along the brick walk. Near the side porch the dogs barked and leaped up at the lamb, scaring both of us.

"Down! Go away, go away," I scolded and hurried to the back door and into the safe kitchen.

"Maa-aaa."

"Lord-a-mercy," Liza said, "whose lamb is that?"

"Mine. Mr. Cline gave her to me. She's only one day old."

"Poor little baby," Liza said, shaking her head.

"Maa-aaa."

"Hold her for me, Liza, while I get a washtub and a blanket."

Washtub on the back porch, blanket in the upstairs cedar chest—

it didn't take long to fetch them both, fast as I was flying.

Gently I laid the lamb on the folded blanket in the tub, and right then Catherine came in.

"Shut the door, quick," I snapped at her. "Don't let the dogs in whatever you do. Look what Mr. Cline gave me."

Catherine dropped to her knees beside the tub. "She's darling, Nan. What are you going to name her?"

"Dee Gee," I answered almost without thinking, "Dee Gee for Delta Gamma. It suits her, don't you think?" Delta Gamma was Ruth's sorority at college. The Dee Gees were a grand bunch, and Catherine and I hoped to belong someday ourselves.

"Perfectly," was the answer.

"Maa-aaa."

"She's starving," I exclaimed in despair. "She was just born this morning and we've got to feed her at once. But how? We've got to have a real baby bottle with a nipple on it."

While we were trying to decide the fastest way to get to the drugstore in the village, whether to go by streetcar, bicycle, or donkey cart, Mr. Cline filled the dining room doorway.

"Come on, girls," he said, "the only thing faster than my horse and buggy is a locomotive."

He was right. That horse really could step and you could tell he liked to go fast, head up, ears pointed, mane rising and falling as he clop, clop, clopped up Edmondson Avenue, the three of us sitting bolt straight in the buggy, me in the middle.

In no time we were back home with half a dozen baby bottles and enough nipples for a flock of orphan lambs. Mr. Cline couldn't buy one of anything.

Dee Gee wouldn't nurse at first, not until I dipped my finger in warm milk and made her taste it. Then she nursed away, her little tail flapping.

Having a lamb was wonderful, but there were a few difficulties. She couldn't stay in the kitchen at night because the dogs slept there, and it wouldn't be fair to make them move when they were there first. Mother wouldn't let us take her to our room, and she was much too young for the barn. After arguing back and forth we decided that for the time being she would stay in the pantry at night and in the kitchen during the day.

Another problem was she had to have a bottle every four hours night and day. We argued about who was to feed her when until Daddy said if he heard another word on the subject he would take the lamb back where she came from. Of course he wouldn't. Even so, from then on we talked in controlled whispers. Finally we decided that I would give her a bottle at ten, two, and six, daytime when I was home, and when I wasn't Mother would. She and Catherine would take turns at night.

Dee Gee grew fast. Before long she was skipping around the lawn. When she was old enough to sleep all night without a bottle, we moved her down to the barn to her own stall, the one with the half door, next to the steps.

Peanuts and Bess took to her at once and she took to them. The only trouble was she could duck under the fence around the field. We had to put Peanuts and Bess out, shut the gate, and keep Dee Gee in the barnyard. Bess didn't mind but Peanuts did. When he was out he wanted to be in, and vice versa. To help matters, we put Bob's old collar on Dee Gee and staked her out on a rope near the house where we could keep an eye out for visiting dogs. Our dogs didn't chase her much now, and when they did it was for fun and she knew it.

By June Dee Gee had a thick wool coat, very heavy for the early spell of hot weather we were having. She lay on her side and panted by the hour. I was worried and said at least a hundred times that she needed shearing. Daddy, Mr. Cline, Mr. Griffith, and Mr. Kreger all said it was better not to shear lambs the first year, but I wouldn't listen.

The heat spell continued and I kept on pestering Daddy to shear the lamb.

Finally he said, "As you choose to ignore the advice of people who

Bess, Dee Gee, Catherine, Mr. Griffith, Mag, and me

know, you must assume the responsibility for the outcome."

"Yes, sir."

"Very well. Tell Mr. Griffith I say shear the lamb." He leveled a steel look at me that almost changed my mind.

"Yes, sir, I'll tell him right now."

I borrowed Catherine's white silk parasol to keep the hot sun off my head and walked over to Mr. Griffith's house. He was taking a nap on the back porch when I got there, head leaning against the wall, mouth open. He snapped it shut when I said hello and seemed pleased to see me. He was not pleased when he heard what I had to say.

"You'll be sorry, Nan," he told me. "She's such a pretty little thing." He shook his head and added, "Well, if your father says so, I'll have to do it."

Feeling uneasy, though not enough to make me change my mind, I went back home.

The next morning right after the milking, Mr. Griffith sheared Dee Gee, with me leaning over his shoulder, my nose close to the sharp shears.

"Watch out, you nicked her!" I exclaimed, grabbing his arm.

"Maaa-aaa."

"Look there, she's bleeding." A small red spot showed on her newly exposed pink skin.

Mr. Griffith straightened up and waved me aside, saying, "Stand back. It's you that's making me nervous. Stand back."

I stepped back an inch or two and watched the rest of the shearing nervously. Thank goodness there was no more blood.

"That does it," Mr. Griffith said and Dee Gee scrambled to her feet. She skipped and gamboled around, flipping her funny shorn tail.

"She's so happy," I said, smiling a wide smile. "Thank you ever so much, Mr. Griffith. Aren't you glad you sheared her?"

"She's happy now," was his disturbing answer.

I watched him go up the hill with the milk bucket, then I stuffed the wool in a gunny sack. Someday, when I had enough, Mr. Cline was going to have it woven into a blanket for me.

That night I woke up cold. A strong wind was threatening the pine trees outside the window and rattling the shutters. I reached for the blanket folded on the foot of the bed, pulled it up and snuggled down under it close to my warm sister. Then all at once I remembered. "Dee Gee!" I shouted, and leaped up, throwing the covers in the air.

Catherine was on her feet almost before I landed. And there was Mother in the doorway, her long black plaits hanging across her shoulder, nightgown on and no slippers she had come so fast.

"What is wrong, Nan?" they both asked and I wailed, "It's cold. Dee Gee will catch pneumonia with no wool on. Oh, why didn't I listen to Daddy and Mr. Griffith! What shall we do?"

"Ask your father," Mother said, flipping the plait around back. "He hasn't come up to bed yet."

I flung my flowered bathrobe around my shoulders, stepped into my slippers, tiptoed fast down the front stairs and looked in the living room. Daddy was reading, the goose-neck light with the dark green shade bent low over his book, the rest of the room in dimness.

Sensing someone was there, he looked up.

"Dee Gee," I said and burst into tears.

He did not say, "I told you so." He did not give me a lecture. He didn't say anything. He closed his book, went to the pantry, took down the lantern from the peg by the icebox, lighted it, and headed for the barn. The dogs and I went with him.

Wind whipped around my legs as I hurried along. Overhead clouds were moving fast, black against the dark sky.

The animals in the barn were surprised to see us in the middle of the night. Peanuts nickered a greeting. Bess, lying down in the straw, turned her head and looked at us with calm trust.

Dee Gee, looking small and helpless in the corner of her stall, maa-aaed softly. Still not saying anything, Daddy handed me the lantern, went in the stall and picked the lamb up in his arms. Then we started back to the house, the light from the lantern making an eerie circle around my feet, the dogs bounding ahead.

Smoke was coming out of Mr. Kreger's chimney, ghost smoke against the dark sky. As we passed his house he was standing in the shadowy doorway. I could see his short nightshirt and pipestem legs.

"Anything wrong, Mr. Hayden?" he asked and for once he didn't spit. "I heard the dogs barking and saw your light go by when I got up to throw a log on my fire. Come bedtime I started a fire to take the chill off. By them clouds we're in for a spell of bad weather."

I lifted the lantern high so he could see Dee Gee in Daddy's arms and told him, "We're taking her indoors where she won't get pneumonia."

To my surprise and Daddy's, Mr. Kreger said, "Hand her here. I'll look out for her till it warms up again."

"Thank you, Kreger, kind of you, I'm sure," Daddy said, handing over the lamb.

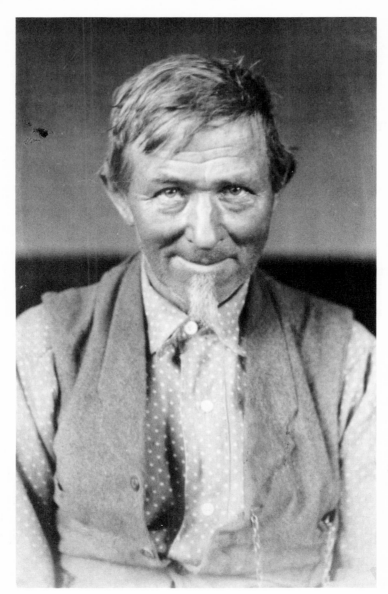

Mr. Kreger

"Maaa-aaa."

As the door closed behind Mr. Kreger and Dee Gee, I said to Daddy, "Imagine him being so hospitable, ornery as he is."

Daddy didn't answer. Instead he stood by the grape arbor near the back door and looked up at the sky. The dogs stood still beside him and so did I. In a little while he went into the house. If the sky had been clear we would have stayed there while Daddy pointed out the North Star, Venus if it was showing, Orion, the Big and Little Dippers.

I wanted to tell him how sorry I was that I'd gone against his judgment about the lamb. I didn't, though. However, before we turned in that night, over a glass of milk and a roast beef sandwich in the kitchen, I looked the message at him and he got it.

To show our appreciation to Mr. Kreger for being so nice to Dee Gee, Catherine and I made him a cake the next day, yellow dough with chocolate icing, his favorite.

Luckily the cold spell was short, over in three days, and Dee Gee went back to the barn without so much as a cold.

twelve

THE PATIENT

ONE SATURDAY IN OCTOBER we had a big day planned. Robbins spent the night at our house and so did Amelie Lefranc, Catherine's best friend. As Ruth was away, Catherine and Amelie slept in her room and Robbins slept with me. Although we talked and talked until Mother made us stop around midnight, we were up early the next morning and through breakfast by seven-thirty.

By eight o'clock Dot, Will, Billy, Landon, and Gladys were there. David and Howard had gone somewhere with their father. The afternoon before we had made a good-sized tent up near the burnt pile out of matting that once ran along the upstairs hall floor. We were going to play Indians and Settlers, with Catherine as the leader of the settlers, and Billy as the Indian chief. Both sides had laid in provisions for lunch.

Right off, before the game got under way, Billy decided he would catch Peanuts and ride him bareback as an Indian pony. He got the bridle off the peg in the barn and went down the hill, whistling.

"Ca-thrin," he shouted from the barnyard almost at once, "come here."

Catherine, in the tent on her hands and knees, poked her head out the door flap and shouted back, "What do you want?"

"Something is wrong with the donkey!"

We all dropped what we were doing and ran, Gladys ten feet behind the rest of us as usual.

Peanuts was standing by the gate looking worried, eyelids half closed, legs sort of spraddled as though they could hardly hold him up.

"Get Mother," Catherine told me, but she didn't have to. I was already on my way to the house.

I burst into the kitchen and ran past Liza to the back steps, nearly knocking her down.

"Mother," I called up, "something awful has happened!"

Mother lost no time coming down. "What's the matter, Nan?" she asked breathlessly, looking me up and down for broken bones.

"Peanuts is sick. He needs a doctor right away."

Mother and Liza looked relieved. "You'd better take a look at the donkey yourself, Miss Emily, before you go calling a doctor on a hearsay," Liza advised.

"You're right, Liza," Mother said. She hurried out the door with me stepping on her heels.

After one look at Peanuts she shook her head. "Poor boy, he is sick. I'll telephone your father and ask him what we should do."

Daddy said he couldn't tell a thing sitting at his desk in town, that we should call Mr. Griffith and ask him.

Mr. Griffith took forever getting there—at least fifteen minutes, and maybe more than twenty. I thought I'd collapse waiting for him; we all did except Gladys who wanted to know about the game of Indians and Settlers. Honestly! Imagine thinking about a game during an emergency.

When Mr. Griffith finally got there he examined Peanuts and said he didn't think there was anything too serious the matter but as I put so much store in him maybe Mother had better call a horse doctor.

"Who?" Mother asked and he didn't know. Bess and Mag had been so well he'd never had to call one.

"How about the doctor who came the day Mr. Polli's horse swelled up?" suggested Catherine. "You remember that day, don't you, Nan?"

Remember it, I'd never forget it. Mr. Polli, a huckster, came to our house once a week with farm things in a wagon pulled by two real big horses. One day when he was there, Liza picking out some good cantaloupes, one of the horses swelled up tight. Mr. Polli told Mother to please telephone a Dr. Young on Johnny Cake Road and tell him to hurry. I remembered the name because the doctor was the opposite of young. Then Mr. Polli unhitched that horse and walked him around the front circle until the doctor came, wouldn't let him stop a second.

Dr. Young said if Mr. Polli hadn't walked the horse it would have died. I wanted to walk Peanuts but Mr. Griffith said, "Leave him be."

"Dr. Young, Mother, that's the name," I said and she hurried to the telephone again.

As Johnny Cake Road was three miles away and there was nothing much anybody could do until the doctor arrived, Catherine, Dot, Gladys, and the boys went up to the tent to wait for him.

Robbins and I climbed the walnut tree by the barnyard fence and sat on the big limb that hung over the fence. Below us, Peanuts stood perfectly still, pitiful. I thought of the white chickens murdered in their beds, Bob killed by accident, and now Peanuts sick. Why didn't that doctor hurry?

After what seemed an eternity, Catherine called out, "Here he comes!" We jumped down and ran to meet an ancient horse, an ancient buggy, and an ancient man.

With everybody standing around in a circle—Mother, Mr. Kreger, all of us children—Dr. Young examined Peanuts thoroughly. He ran a gentle hand down the donkey's side, under his belly. He looked in his mouth, lifted his eyelids and looked at his eyes, Peanuts returning the look mournfully.

"I'll need a bucket of water, please, Ma'am," the doctor said to Mother. Right away Robbins and I ran to the spring and fetched it, water sloshing on our legs, we were in such a hurry.

Dr. Young poured some medicine in the water, held Peanuts' nose in the air and poured a quart of the mixture down his throat. Peanuts, wall-eyed with nerves, swallowed.

"It will take about three minutes for the remedy to have the desired effect," the doctor said, taking a large gold watch out of his pocket.

When the three minutes were up, he snapped the watch shut and Peanuts belched. There never was such a belch. Leaves on the tree limb overhead trembled with it. It outdid Mr. Kreger at his worst.

Billy rolled on the grass kicking his heels and laughing, which I thought extremely rude.

"Ma'am," said Dr. Young turning to Mother, "if the patient has not improved considerably by tomorrow, please notify me."

Mother said she would.

That one day I was glad when everybody went home, even Robbins, so Catherine and I could give our full attention to Peanuts. Not that there was anything we could do for him. We stayed nearby, kept him company, and told him from time to time that he would feel better soon. He didn't want us to bathe his forehead with cold towels dipped in water. We tried it and he definitely didn't. He didn't want his back scratched, either, or anything to eat, not even at suppertime.

The next morning he was not better. When he wasn't cribbing on the chicken house windowsill he was biting his own knees. He had them raw, blood running down his leg. I was so worried about him and of course the doctor had to come again.

This time he covered the raw sores with yellow salve, bandaged the knees, and told us to make sure the bandages stayed in place.

Before the doctor's buggy was out of sight Peanuts had pulled one bandage loose with his large teeth and was working on the other one. Catherine and I were so busy trying to put the bandages back on and make him stop pulling at them, we did not notice that the doctor had left the barnyard gate open.

Bess strolled back to Mr. Griffith's house, which really distressed me because I thought she liked living at our house. It wasn't until Mr. Griffith brought her back, which he did right away, that we discovered that Dee Gee was missing.

By the time we found her, taking a rest under the hammock beside the front porch, she had eaten a whole row of petunias in full bloom, Mother's favorite white ones, enough to give her a stomachache.

When we got back to Peanuts both bandages were down around his ankles and he was biting his knees again. I was in despair; Catherine, too. We didn't know what to do next.

It was Mr. Kreger who solved the problem.

"If the mule was mine, and I'm glad to say he ain't, I'd put pants on him so's he couldn't get at them bandages," he said when he came into the kitchen for his lunch.

It was a fine idea and I told Mr. Kreger so. However, thinking it up was all Mr. Kreger would do about it. He refused to lend Peanuts a pair of pants, said a flat "No" when I suggested it. As it turned out, I was glad he did because Mother let us borrow Daddy's baggy, faded blue denims.

Putting pants on the donkey was not easy. We struggled and struggled getting nowhere and were about to give up when Catherine thought of ripping the back seam, which was a big help. After that we were able to ease one hoof in at a time, first rubbing the back of the leg to make him lift it.

"What you need is suspenders," said Mr. Griffith, strolling up with the milk bucket.

"Yes," we both said, and while we took turns holding the pants up, he went home, walking fast for him, and brought us purple suspenders with little brass sliders.

Peanuts looked charming dressed up, and to our joy he forgot his knees. Everybody came to see him in pants, children and grownups. Even Grandma and Auntie trailed down the hill, their skirts bending the grass.

Grandma was amused and Auntie said, "Oh, I do wish Father were alive to see the donkey with us."

I wished hard that she would get to Venice some day. Everybody should have what he wants most. I had what I wanted: Dee Gee and Bess were well and happy, the cat and kittens had good homes, and most important of all, Peanuts was getting over whatever it was he had had.

But now I had something I didn't want—a stiff neck. It was just a slight one, not enough to pull my head to one side, and the rest of me felt fine. Most likely it would be gone by tomorrow.

thirteen

ALWAYS GIVE WATER
ALWAYS GIVE SHADE

BY MORNING MY NECK WAS STIFFER and hurt. I didn't mention it to anybody because what I hated most, next to cruelty, was not feeling good. However, as I couldn't hold my head straight during breakfast, the family caught on without being told. Nobody said anything, knowing how I felt about such things. Still, worried glances that didn't match the conversation shot back and forth across the table and I knew they knew.

After breakfast I walked slowly down to the barn to feed the animals and Catherine went with me. We staked Peanuts out on a rope under the walnut tree where the grass was especially luscious, and tied Dee Gee nearby so she could reach some of it too.

"I'll fill the water buckets today," Catherine told me, her way of saying she was sorry about the neck.

I nodded, which hurt somewhat, then went on to the house and up to our room. Mother must have heard me throw myself across the bed, for I'd hardly landed when she came in and held out her hand. In it was the cutest little celluloid Kewpie no bigger than my thumb.

"It has been in my glove box for so long, Nan," she said, "I'd forgotten it was there."

"It's by far the smallest one I've ever seen," I said, getting to my feet. "I'll make it a dress right now."

"Good idea."

I rummaged around in my sewing box and found some apple-green ribbon, real pretty, and a strip of lace.

That day I was able to go downstairs to lunch and dinner. Not the next day, though, because my neck really hurt and my left ear ached. Mother telephoned Dr. Wisner, our family doctor, to come out to see me. After examining me very carefully, he said I didn't have the mumps, and he couldn't say what I did have. He gave me some sugar pills in a little bottle to play with and told me to stay in bed all day.

The next day I was no better and Dr. Wisner came by again. This time he shook his head in a worried way and said he'd like to have another doctor see me. Mother and Daddy agreed.

So, after several telephone calls, it was decided that I would go to the Union Protestant Infirmary, an old hospital in Baltimore where the great Dr. J. M. T. Finney was head surgeon. He would look at me there and have some tests made, things like that. Mr. Yardley would drive Mother and me to the hospital ten o'clock the next morning.

I had never been in a hospital, not even to visit somebody, and I didn't want to go. I wasn't scared, though, just felt uneasy not knowing what to expect.

Downtown Baltimore

That night, unable to sleep, I thrashed around and kept calling for Mother. Catherine was sleeping in the guest room for the time being. After coming upstairs to comfort me for the tenth time, Mother stayed and rested on top of the covers beside me. She didn't sleep, either. By the dim light coming through the door from the hall I could see her eyes wide open, looking at me.

"It's only for tests," I told her and she said, "I know, dear. Go to sleep. I'm here." That's all we said the rest of the night. I lay there hurting, listening to squirrels bowling with walnuts in the walls. Once the house itself stretched, making boards creak downstairs.

Finally morning came. By nine-thirty I was dressed, suitcase packed: night things, the new Kewpie in her devastating new dress, two other Kewpies to keep her company, seventeen of my best paper dolls, the new *St. Nicholas* magazine, *Alice in Wonderland* (I was on page 38, reading it for the third time), a notebook and pencil in case I wanted to write a poem or something, and crayons and sketch pad for drawing. Although I didn't feel like doing anything right then, I wanted to be ready the second I did.

I also wanted very much to say good-bye to my animals, but I didn't; the barn seemed too far away. Before going downstairs, I stopped in the back room and made a sign in black letters on one of Mother's gray mounts:

ALWAYS GIVE WATER, ALWAYS GIVE SHADE

For such an important sign I was sure she wouldn't mind. I left it on the hall table beside the telephone where everybody was bound to see it.

Now I was ready to go and Mr. Yardley was right on time.

"Good-bye, Liza, good-bye, Catherine," I called as I walked out the front door to the automobile. "I'll see you soon."

We drove to town slowly to avoid unnecessary bumps. At the hospital I rode in a wheelchair pushed by a nurse down a long hall, in an elevator up, up, then down another hall, which would have been fun under other circumstances.

My room was pretty, all blue—blue walls, blue bed, blue chair, everything blue. A pretty nurse in a darker blue uniform, white apron, and cap helped me undress and get into bed. A young doctor came next and asked as many questions as the policeman that day the chickens were murdered. Then he looked down my throat, took a drop of blood from the end of my finger, and measured my blood pressure with a funny band around my arm which he blew up with something like a bicycle pump.

Mother stayed with me until the night nurse came on duty, and was back by eight-thirty the next morning.

In the early afternoon Dr. Finney came in walking briskly, a stocky man with brown hair, not tall. I trusted him completely at once.

"Good morning, Nan," he said, looking at me with gray eyes that had fun in them and sympathy, smart eyes and very kind. "Let's take a look at that neck."

Sitting upright, knees bent Indian fashion, I raised my chin as far as I could, which wasn't far, and he felt around with expert fingers the way Dr. Young had felt Peanuts. "Hurt there?"

"Yes, sir."

"Here?"

"Yes, but not as much."

"Here?"

"No, sir."

"Well," he clipped the word off short, "tomorrow we'll go in there and see what's causing the trouble. We want to get rid of this business once and for all."

"You mean you're going to operate?" I asked, swallowing hard.

He nodded vigorously and said, "First thing in the morning."

We shook hands and he left the room. I could hear him talking to Mother outside the door for a while, then go briskly down the hall.

I didn't like that night much—sounds I wasn't used to, people walking by the door, missing home, hurting in spite of some brown medicine that was supposed to stop the hurt and put me to sleep.

When Mother came in the next morning I had on a funny hospital nightgown, real short, open down the back, long sleeves. "Don't worry, Mother. Doctor Finney knows what he's doing. I'll be well in no time, you'll see," I told her, but she went right on worrying.

Promptly at nine I rode on what looked like an ironing board with wheels to a small white room on the sixth floor that smelled somewhat like Mother's darkroom. "Ether," explained the nurse and she patted my arm in a friendly way, though I'd never seen her before.

Right then Dr. Finney came in wearing a white gown quite like mine only longer and belted. "Ready, Nan?" he asked.

"Yes," I answered, my heart pounding.

While a young doctor, a new one, held one hand, the nurse holding the other, somebody behind me put a cone over my nose and said, "Start at ninety-nine and count backwards."

"Ninety-eight, ninety-seven, ninety-six"—the ether smelled real strong now—"ninety-five, ninety . . ."

The next thing I knew the operation was over and I was back in my blue bed in the blue room yelling "Mother!" louder than Peanuts ever brayed for me. She was there. As soon as I could get the room in focus I saw her at the foot of the bed talking with Dr. Finney. He was saying, "From the sound of her voice I'd say she was in fine shape, Mrs. Hayden."

Then to my humiliation, I threw up. Immediately, though, there was a nurse at my side with a curved basin, ready to help.

"You'll feel better now," she said and she was right. The earache had gone, the unbearable hurt in my neck had gone, too, and in its place a new one that was bearable under a fat bandage.

For two days I lay flat, wasting time, doing absolutely nothing. I did ask about my animals, and Mother said they were getting along very well. Then she read to me by the hour and I halfway listened, dropping off to sleep in the middle of a sentence, waking to find the thread of plot lost.

Mother was excellent at catching you up on a plot. One question and she'd nail it down in a few words. She came every day. Daddy came on his way home from the office, sat by the window and read his newspaper for exactly twenty minutes by his watch open on the foot of the bed. Grandma and Auntie came too, and so did Mr. Yardley.

Catherine did not come because children weren't supposed to. Robbins sent cards and so did Miss Smith and the rest of the class at school, all the names in a row. And Ruth sent a great present, ten presents in a box to open one at a time, one each day.

The third day after the operation I began to exercise parts of myself. Daddy said that if you didn't, your muscles, including your head, would get rusty and I didn't want that to happen. I did wand drills with my arms and after kicking back the covers air-bicycled with both feet, fast as I could with already slightly rusty legs.

I wasn't sick, just healing, getting over the operation. Meals on trays were fun, hot things covered with metal lids, ice cream almost every day. Between meals I played with the Kewpies, pretending they were nurses walking back and forth across my chest. I drew some, read some, and played cards with Dr. King, the doctor in charge of our hall, whenever he wasn't too busy.

It wasn't all fun, though, because my neck was awfully sore, a raw worked-over soreness. Dr. Finney made me rest back on the pillow quite a lot and wouldn't let me turn my head. One good thing: he told Mother he was pretty sure he'd found what was causing the trouble, and that it wouldn't come back again.

One day, feeling extra frisky, I got out of bed, put on my kimono and slippers, and walked down the hall. Dr. Finney had told me there were other children in the hospital and I wanted to meet them.

I pushed open the door that said Children's Ward and stepped in. Fourteen beds lined the large, bright room. "Hello," I said to the children in the beds. "My name is Nan Hayden. I'm your neighbor."

"Could you put a record on the victrola?" said a boy near the door, a thin boy whose leg was sticking up in the air, a weight on a pully keeping it there.

"Make it 'Stars and Stripes Forever,'" called out a fat boy across the room and a girl said, "Yes, that's a good one."

I put the record they wanted on the big victrola in the middle of the ward, cranked the handle, set the needle, and Sousa's band began to da *da*, da da *da*, da da *da*, through the big open-faced horn.

The fat boy thumped the mattress with his heels keeping time, and a little boy whose head was completely bandaged banged on the side of his crib with an iron train. One boy lay perfectly still, looking up, and a girl leaned on the foot of her crib, her head on her arms, tears smeared all over her face.

While I was standing there, waiting to put on another record, Miss Barnsley, the head nurse, came hurrying in. "Come along, Nan," she said. "Dr. Finney is in your room waiting to change your dressing."

I followed her out, stopping to look back once at the other children. I hoped hard that the doctors would fix them up the way they'd fixed me.

The dressing really was painful. I cried some, even though I didn't want to. Dr. Finney said he would have cried too if I'd been in his shoes and he'd been in mine. That made me laugh because Miss Barnsley had taken my slippers off and there were my bare feet on top of the bedspread.

"When am I going home?" I asked Dr. Finney while he was putting on a fresh bandage.

"What's the hurry, Nan?" he said. "From what I hear you're having a good time."

"I am, but I need to get home." I told him about Peanuts, Dee Gee, Bess, and how Catherine was taking care of things for me.

He nodded his head and said, "We'll talk about going home when I see you again on Monday. All right?"

"Yes, sir."

Dr. Finney stuck down the last strip of adhesive and left the room, the nurse following him down the hall.

Time went by fast. When I wasn't visiting the children in the ward I was playing paper dolls or with the Kewpies, or drawing, reading, or playing games. Dr. King was a champion gin rummy player. I couldn't beat him, not even one game.

Monday, when Dr. Finney came to see me, I waited until the dressing was over before asking him when I was going home. This time he gave me a generous smile. "How does tomorrow sound?"

Tomorrow! Nothing could have sounded better. And I was just about to tell him so when he added: "But you must promise to come back to the dispensary a week from today, so we can see how the neck is healing."

"Oh yes, Dr. Finney! I'll come back *ten* times if you want me to." I meant it, too.

After he left, I had to lie still a while, my head on the pillow, to get over the dressing. As soon as the hurting faded, I got up and went down the hall to spread the good news—to Miss Barnsley standing by the desk near the elevator, to the head nurse behind the desk, Dr. King bent over a report he was writing, a man pushing a dust mop wide as the hall itself, and the elevator man when the elevator stopped at our floor.

Then I walked fast to the children's ward, stretching my chin up and down to get used to the new bandage.

"Hi," I said from the door, "guess what?"

"What?"

I told them and then put one of my favorite records on the victrola. I cranked the handle so vigorously the whole thing nearly tipped over, and sang at the top of my voice with the other children:

Roamin' in the gloamin'
On the bonnie banks o' Clyde
Roamin' in the gloamin'
With my lassie by my side.

That night I was far too excited to sleep. I lay in the dark and saw pictures in my head taken by my camera eyes. The first was Nancy's Fancy in spring: the apple orchard in pink bloom, the big clapboard house with its four handsome red brick chimneys looking across the green lawn, Mr. Kreger's house behind it, and still farther back the gray barn trimmed in jelly-bag red.

The next picture I saw, taken inside the house, was of the attic where Catherine and I played sometimes on rainy afternoons. I could see the dollhouse clearly and the boxes of Christmas tree balls and tinsel. In the corner was the trunk where Grandfather's dress suit lay in moth balls, the man who wore it to parties dead longer than Bob and the White Leghorns.

The last picture I saw before I went to sleep was a group portrait of Mother, Daddy, Ruth, Catherine, Grandma, Auntie, Liza, Mr. Kreger, and Mr. Griffith, with Dee Gee, Bess, the dogs, Billy, Jenny, and the other chickens in the background. Peanuts was standing in the foreground, looking for me.

Tomorrow he'd see me and not in a picture either. Tomorrow he'd *really* see me and so would everybody else at Nancy's Fancy. And I'd see them.

Tomorrow I was going home, in pretty good shape, too, ready to pitch in and catch up on lost time.